DISCHARGE PATTERNS OF SINGLE FIBERS IN THE CAT'S AUDITORY NERVE

DISCHARGE PATTERNS OF SINGLE FIBERS IN THE CAT'S AUDITORY NERVE

NELSON YUAN-SHENG KIANG

with the assistance of
Takeshi Watanabe, Eleanor C. Thomas, and Louise F. Clark

RESEARCH MONOGRAPH NO. 35
THE M.I.T. PRESS, CAMBRIDGE, MASSACHUSETTS

Acknowledgment

The Eaton-Peabody Laboratory of Auditory Physiology is jointly operated by the Massachusetts Institute of Technology and the Massachusetts Eye and Ear Infirmary. The Research Laboratory of Electronics of the Massachusetts Institute of Technology is an interdepartmental laboratory in which faculty members and graduate students from numerous academic departments conduct research.

The research reported in this document was supported in part by private funds, in part by the National Institutes of Health (grant NB-01344 to the Eaton-Peabody Laboratory), and in part by funds made available through the Research Laboratory of Electronics from support extended by the JOINT SERVICES ELECTRONICS PROGRAMS (U.S. Army, U.S. Navy, and U.S. Air Force) under Contract No. DA36-039-AMC-03200(E), the National Science Foundation (Grant GP-2495), the National Institutes of Health (Grant MH-04737-05), and the National Aeronautics and Space Administration (Grant NsG-496).

This is Special Technical Report Number 13 of the Research Laboratory of Electronics of the Massachusetts Institute of Technology.

Foreword

There has long been a need in science and engineering for systematic publication of research studies larger in scope than a journal article but less ambitious than a finished book. Much valuable work of this kind is now published only in a semiprivate way, perhaps as a laboratory report, and so may not find its proper place in the literature of the field. The present contribution is the thirty-fifth of the M.I.T. Press Research Monographs, which we hope will make selected timely and important research studies readily accessible to libraries and to the independent worker.

J. A. STRATTON

Author's Preface

Many individuals have contributed to the work described in this monograph. R. M. Brown, A. H. Crist, and the staff of the TX-O computer at the Massachusetts Institute of Technology have been most helpful with technical problems. M. A. Saunders, A. N. Backus, and M. R. Kiang have helped with the preparation of the figures and manuscript. It is a pleasure to acknowledge the assistance rendered by Dr. W. T. Peake, Dr. T. F. Weiss, and Dr. Francis S. Wiener in reading portions of the manuscript, although they cannot be held responsible for the published version. Dr. L. A. Schall, Dr. F. S. Weille, Dr. P. E. Meltzer, Dr. M. H. Lurie, Dr. H. F. Schuknecht, and Dr. J. W. Irwin have contributed much toward making this work possible. Finally, special thanks are due Professor W. A. Rosenblith for his constant guidance and support.

This monograph should be considered an interim report on a continuing research project. By the time that the report is published, some of the material may already be obsolete. We have, therefore, tried to be conservative in our presentation of data and interpretations.

Boston, Massachusetts
September, 1965   NELSON YUAN-SHENG KIANG

Preface

This monograph reports experiments on single auditory nerve fibers conducted over a period of six years. Others have reported experiments on the behavior of primary auditory units in the cat, although there exists no published record of as extensive and systematic a series of experiments in this area. There have, of course, also been numerous papers and books on researches involving the cooperation of staff members of medical institutions and members of departments and laboratories of a scientifically oriented university. However, there is an interesting bit of history connected with the origin of this particular monograph.

Early in 1950, Dr. Leroy A. Schall, then Chief of Otolaryngology at the Massachusetts Eye and Ear Infirmary and LeCompte Professor of Otology at the Harvard Medical School, felt the need to bring basic investigations into the hospital environment. Three distinguished otologists, Drs. Moses H. Lurie,* Dr. Philip E. Meltzer, and Dr. Francis L. Weille on the Infirmary's staff, agreed enthusiastically with a plan that would locate a long-range program of basic research in hearing in the Massachusetts Eye and Ear Infirmary. They hoped that the hospital environment would tend to suggest significant problems and that young physicians would benefit from contact with basic research while engaged in clinical training.

---

*In the 1930's and 40's, Dr. Lurie, together with his Harvard colleagues Dr. H. Davis and Professor S. S. Stevens, made important contributions to the understanding of the anatomy and physiology of the auditory system.

Dr. Weille was instrumental in obtaining the cooperation of the M.I.T. Administration in the mid-1950's, and shortly thereafter the first joint efforts were undertaken by staff members at both institutions. After a period of about a year, during which several members of the Communications Biophysics Group in M.I.T.'s Research Laboratory of Electronics (R.L.E.) acted as part-time consultants to the Massachusetts Eye and Ear Infirmary group, it became clear that a different form of cooperation was required if a program of sufficient scope and potential impact upon the hospital environment was to be initiated.

The two institutions agreed on submitting a common proposal to the National Institutes of Health, with the research to be conducted primarily at the Massachusetts Eye and Ear Infirmary but with several of the more technical activities of the program carried out in the R.L.E. The Board of Managers of the Massachusetts Eye and Ear Infirmary designated half of the Infirmary's available land for the construction of a building that is now known as the Eaton-Peabody Laboratory of Auditory Physiology. Funds for this building came from private donors; the National Institutes of Health and several public-spirited citizens have generously supported an expanding program of research.

From the inception of this program on the neurophysiology of the auditory system, it was clear that its uniqueness would be derived from a judicious blending of contemporary biological and engineering techniques. The author of this monograph was primarily responsible for the development of an appropriate experimental style in which anatomy, physiology, acoustics, communications and computer engineering all contribute to the study of problems that had their origin in clinical findings or psycho-acoustic experiments. These circumstances and the scope of this series of research monographs preclude a full discussion of the problems of the auditory system from the viewpoints of the many disciplines involved in the study of this system. Hence this monograph tries to communicate a set of experimental findings to an audience that is anything but narrowly tuned. It does not build upon the background of a single discipline; indeed, it touches upon topics which deal with the functioning of the auditory nerve in relation to the concerns of a number of fields and specialties.

Since this monograph has been long in the making, many people have participated in the collection and analysis of the data. Those who had the largest share in this task are identified on the title page. During Dr. Watanabe's two-year visit he was a full-fledged collaborator in the research team, contributing an element of international collaboration. He came from and returned to the Tokyo Medical and

Dental University, where he is a member of the Physiology Department headed by Professor Y. Katsuki.

Throughout the years the cooperation between the Institute and the Infirmary, involving both men and resources, has been exceptionally harmonious. When Dr. Harold F. Schuknecht succeeded Dr. Schall (who now enjoys emeritus status), the new chief of service continued his predecessor's effective support of the research program. There is every reason to assume that this interinstitutional cooperative program will continue to be successful. It derives its strength from common and complementary, scientific and humanitarian motivations. It is a unique reflection of the contemporary Boston scene: there is a mixture of medicine, science, and technology, there is support from both public and private funds, and there are administrative officials willing to make arrangements so that the work may proceed.

WALTER A. ROSENBLITH
Massachusetts Institute of Technology

JOHN S. IRWIN
Massachusetts Eye and Ear Infirmary

Contents

DISCHARGE PATTERNS OF SINGLE FIBERS
IN THE CAT'S AUDITORY NERVE

1. Introduction

The physiological processes underlying normal mammalian hearing are initiated when sound enters the external ear and sets into motion the tympanic membrane with its attached chain of middle-ear ossicles. The last bone in this chain, the stapes, is seated in a membranous opening, the oval window of the cochlea. The cochlea, or inner ear, is a fluid-filled bony structure that contains the specialized auditory receptor elements and the peripheral portions of the auditory nerve. The more central parts of the auditory nerve fibers exit from the cochlea and project into the cochlear nucleus of the brain. The activity in this nerve constitutes the first stage of the neural processes that underlie hearing.

Neurophysiology has at times been described as data-rich and theory-poor. The neurophysiology of hearing however may almost be described as speculation-rich and data-poor. There is a serious lack of systematic data at virtually every level of the auditory system. When we undertook our research program, only one series of experiments on responses in single auditory nerve fibers had been published (Tasaki, 1954; Tasaki and Davis, 1955).* We felt that the impor-

* The single-unit responses described by Galambos and Davis in earlier studies (1943, 1944) appear now to have been recorded from higher-order neurons in the cochlear nucleus (1948). Thus, although Galambos and Davis were pioneers in the development of both concepts and experimental procedures that later led directly to studies such as ours, the first undisputed demonstrations of activity recorded from single auditory nerve fibers are properly credited to Tasaki (1954).

1

tance of the auditory nerve for hearing demanded more detailed knowledge of its responses. Thus a project was started that is still active, for each discovery raised many more new questions. This monograph represents a summary of some of the results to date and our tentative conclusions.

The plan of this monograph is as follows: first, the methods will be described; next, the results will be presented within a framework that indicates the purpose and significance of each series of experiments; finally, the more general aspects of interpretation and some speculations will be left for Chapter 10 under the heading of "Discussion."

The figures constitute the heart of this report. They have been arranged so that an experienced student of auditory physiology should be able to follow the story even without the text. We have tried to supply sufficiently detailed information on experimental procedures and results so that our measurements may be checked by future experimenters.

We do not intend to review the literature concerning peripheral auditory physiology because a number of excellent partial summaries exist (Stevens and Davis, 1938; Wever, 1949; Fletcher, 1953; Helmholtz, 1954; Wever and Lawrence, 1954; Davis, 1957; Békésy, 1960). The reader is referred especially to Wever's *Theory of Hearing* (1949) for a historical introduction to the subject.

One of our long-range objectives has been to accumulate a library of recorded data that may be reexamined and processed in different ways. Most of the original recordings are available on magnetic tape, and already several of our colleagues particularly interested in model making have used them. This taped library also permits an immediate check on possible biases that may have been introduced in the selection of data to be published. Bias remains, of course, in the selection of data that were recorded.

We have made a preliminary report on stimulus coding in the auditory nerve based on an earlier series of animals (Kiang, Watanabe, Thomas, and Clark, 1962), but none of the data presented here have been previously published.

2. Methods

2.1 Animals and Surgical Procedures

We first had to choose an appropriate animal for study. Since the structure of the cochlea and auditory nerve follows the same general plan in all mammals, our final choice of the cat *(Felis catus)* was based on the extensive anatomical, physiological, and behavioral data that are available for this species.

It is well known that humans show hearing losses as a result of both exposure to noise and aging (Glorig and Nixon, 1960). If similar effects are present in cats, our results might well have been contaminated by cats with abnormal hearing. We therefore established an animal farm in Rangely, Maine, where we were able to obtain young adult cats (1 to 2 years) from farms located in the surrounding countryside, a sparsely populated region that is relatively free from noise of high levels. We selected only healthy cats with clean external ear canals. The gross electric potentials of the cochlea and auditory nerve were always checked for threshold. Data from preliminary developmental stages of our work or from cats showing any signs of abnormal health were excluded from this report. Thus the results reported here are based on approximately 1500 units obtained from more than 50 "certified normal" cats.

The animals were anesthetized with intraperitoneal injections of dial-urethane. Normal saline (60 to 100 cc) was routinely injected subcutaneously, and penicillin (100,000 units) was injected intramuscularly. A rectal thermometer was used to monitor the animal's body temperature, which was maintained at 37 to 39°C. After a cannula was inserted into the trachea and the external ear canals cut near the tympanic membrane, the animal was placed in a head-holder with hollow earbars inserted into the central ends of the cut ear canals. The bulla on the side to be stimulated was opened, exposing the cochlea, and the posterior fossa on the same side was opened from a dorsal approach. The cerebellum was retracted to expose the auditory nerve and cochlear nucleus. Gentle traction on the cerebellum frequently made it easier to see the auditory nerve exiting from the internal auditory meatus. Insertion of the micro-electrode into the nerve was always accomplished under direct visual control with the aid of a dissecting microscope.

2.2   Stimulus-Generating and Response-Recording Equipment

After these surgical preliminaries we moved the preparation into a double-walled chamber specially constructed for acoustic isolation

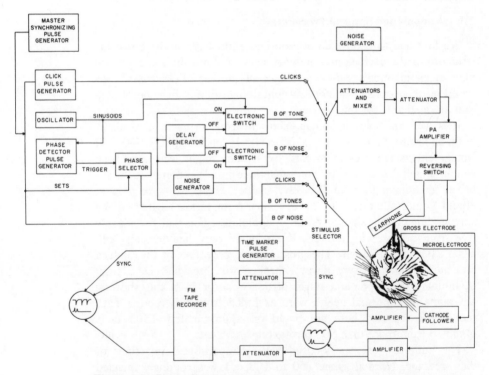

Figure 2.1   Block diagram of the equipment for generating stimuli and re-cording responses.

and electrical shielding. During recordings the animal was alone in the chamber, with all manipulation of electronic equipment and movement of the micropipette controlled remotely to minimize extraneous sounds. A block diagram of the stimulus-generating and response-recording equipment is given in Figure 2.1. The equipment was capable of producing the following stimuli, either singly or mixed:

1. Clicks of controllable polarity, duration, rate, and level.
2. Pure tones of controllable frequency and level.
3. Noise of controllable bandwidth and level.
4. Bursts of tone with controllable rise and fall times, phase of onset, burst duration, burst rate, and frequency and level of the tone.
5. Bursts of noise with controllable rise and fall times, burst duration, and burst rate, as well as bandwidth and level of noise.

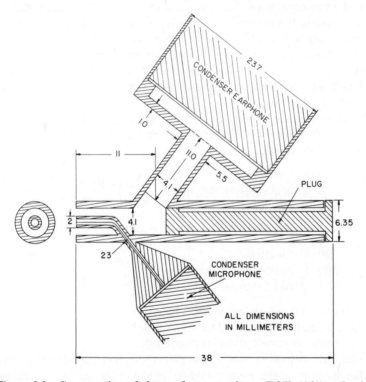

Figure 2.2   Cross section of the condenser earphone (B&K 4161) and microphone (B&K) for delivering and monitoring acoustic stimuli.

The open tube at the left containing the probe tube is also shown in a "head-on" view. During experiments the cavities are packed with nonabsorbent cotton. When dynamic earphones (PDR-10) were used, the plug was removed and a plastic tube connected to the earphone was inserted into the coupler.

In the early experiments stimuli were delivered by PDR-10 dynamic earphones. A plastic tube coupled the earphone to the hollow earbars of the headholder; the total path length from earphone diaphragm to tympanic membrane was approximately 10 cm. PDR-10 earphone I was used in experiments on Cats 250 to 278, PDR-10 earphone II in experiments on Cats 279 to 290. In subsequent experiments stimuli were delivered by Brüel and Kjaer 1″ condenser microphones used as earphones. In these experiments we used a smaller condenser microphone to measure the sound-pressure levels near the eardrum (Figure 2.2).

Calibration curves for both dynamic and condenser earphones are given in Figure 2.3. Although the dynamic range of the condenser earphones is smaller, the calibration curves are smoother and the acoustic clicks show less ringing. These differences are partly a function of earphone characteristics and partly a result of the damping of the condenser earphone system with nonabsorbent cotton. Unlike dynamic earphones, which showed great variation for different samples, the condenser earphones showed highly reproducible characteristics and were easily interchangeable. The calibration curves will enable those interested to convert from voltages to sound-pressure levels for tonal stimuli.

Stimulus levels will be given in terms of input voltages to the earphones. Unless otherwise specified, the two types of earphones have the following reference levels:

$$
\left.\begin{array}{l}
\text{4 V for clicks} \\
\text{8 V peak-to-peak for tones} \\
\text{1 V rms for noise}
\end{array}\right\} \quad \text{Into PDR-10 dynamic earphones}
$$

and

$$
\left.\begin{array}{l}
\text{100 V for clicks} \\
\text{200 V peak-to-peak for tones} \\
\text{70.7 V rms for noise}
\end{array}\right\} \quad \text{Into the condenser earphones}
$$

Since there is no convenient method for measuring the acoustic power of these stimuli, the term "intensity" will be used only in a more general sense to denote stimulus magnitude.

After the acoustic system was in place, we placed a gross electrode on the bone near the round window of the cochlea. This electrode enabled us to record microphonic and gross neural potentials from the cochlea and served as a valuable monitor of the condition of the preparation. This control was particularly important with respect to high-intensity stimuli.

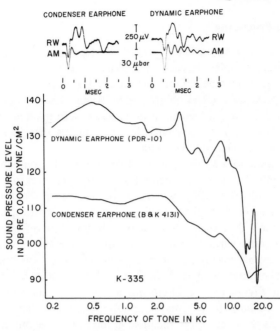

Figure 2.3 Typical sound-pressure calibration curves using the acoustic system of Figure 2.2.

At the top of the figure the electric responses of the round window (RW) and the responses of the acoustic monitor (AM) to clicks generated by both earphones are shown. The electric input to each earphone was a 100-μsec pulse. Input to condenser earphone, 10-V peak. Input to dynamic earphone, .04-V peak. Below these traces the sound-pressure levels of the output of the 2 earphones are shown as a function of frequency. The sound-pressure levels are measured at the tympanic membrane using the arrangement shown in Figure 2.2. These curves were obtained for an attenuator setting of −10 db. Reference level for condenser earphone, 200 V P-P. Reference level for dynamic earphone, 8 V P-P.

The microelectrodes for single-unit recording were 3*M*, KCl-filled micropipettes with resistances in the 20- to 80-megohm range. Each micropipette was positioned under visual observation to make contact with the surface of the nerve. We made all subsequent linear movements of the micropipette from the outer chamber by using a remote-control hydraulic micromanipulator.

The responses from single units were recorded on one channel of an FM tape recorder, the round–window responses were recorded on a second parallel channel, and stimulus-time markers were recorded on a third channel. The passband of the entire recording system was normally 7 to 5000 cps.

2.3 Data-Processing

After each experiment we replayed the taped records and photographed short samples of each run. When required, round–window responses were averaged. Our techniques for averaging have been described previously (Rosenblith, 1959; Kiang, 1961). Photographs of the unit data gave information on spike waveforms and variability of responses and served as a basis for determining the types of computations that would later be made.

The computations were performed on the TX-O computer at the Massachusetts Institute of Technology. For each run of data the processed results were displayed (usually in the form of histograms) on an oscilloscope and photographed. For our purposes a histogram is a bar graph that shows a frequency distribution of events as a function of some variable, and the height of each bar represents the number of events that occur in that particular range (or bin) of the variable. The abscissa of each histogram has the dimension of time (except for Figure 8.10). There are always 128 time bins in each histogram, 16 bins to each major horizontal division. The bin width is always given in msec on the histograms, and the full horizontal scale is simply the bin width multiplied by 128.

The two types of histograms that proved most useful have been described in detail elsewhere (Gerstein and Kiang, 1960). A post-stimulus-time histogram (PST histogram) is a display of the time distribution of unit spike discharges relative to the stimulus-time marker. Each stimulus marker resets the computer's "clock" to zero so that each histogram represents a summation over repeated stimuli presentations. In our studies the stimulus-time markers were synchronized with some aspect of the electrical signals delivered to the earphone. Thus, the time markers for clicks were synchronized with the electric pulse; time markers for tone and noise bursts, with the onset of the bursts; and the time markers for continuous tones, with the positive zero crossings of the sinusoids. Unlike the PST histograms, the interspike-interval histograms display the distribution of intervals between successive unit discharges without regard for the presence of a stimulus.

The initial slope of each discharge triggers a special pulse which is delivered to the computer for processing; excessive baseline fluctuations were eliminated by the use of a high-pass electronic filter. Our results show that the same data yield the same histograms even when the computations are made several years apart. The precision of the computation is such that errors of more than one bin are not found at bin widths of 0.063 msec (the smallest bin widths used in this study).

Both types of histograms share certain conventions in labeling. The letters and numbers on the top line of each histogram give the bin width, location of the data on the tape, and the stimulus condition. Many histograms are identified in the upper left section by a "1" for a PST histogram or an "O" for an interval histogram. The uppermost of these numbers below the top line of the histogram is a code number indicating the cat, the unit, and the picture number. The second number represents the number of stimulus markers on that particular segment of tape. (This number appears even in histograms of spontaneous activity, since dummy stimulus markers are then placed on the tape.) The third number gives the total number of spike discharges on that segment of tape. Histograms not identified with either a "1" or "O" were computed with an earlier program for the computer. In these histograms the first bin is occupied by a bar that indicates the bin width. A number in the PST histogram then shows the number of spikes, and a number in the interval histograms shows the number of stimulus markers. Unless specified, each histogram represents one minute of recorded data.

Computations other than PST and interval histograms will be introduced with the results because they are either obvious or used too infrequently to justify inclusion in a general discussion of methods.

3. Spatial Organization of the Auditory Nerve

3.1 A Brief Review of the Anatomy of the Auditory Nerve

Any physiological study of the auditory nerve must begin with consideration of the anatomy of the cat's cochlea and auditory nerve.* The cochlea consists of a long bony canal that coils from base to apex with decreasing radius of curvature and resembles a snail shell in appearance. In cross section (Figure 3.1) the canal is divided into three fluid-filled compartments. The middle compartment, the scala media, is formed by the basilar and Reissner's membranes. The scala tympani is situated on the basilar membrane side, the scala vestibuli on the Reissner's membrane side. At the apex of the cochlea the scala vestibuli and scala tympani are connected by a narrow channel, the helicotrema. At the base of the cochlea the footplate of the stapes covers the oval window at the end of the scala vestibuli, while the scala tympani ends in the round window. When the stapes pushes into the scala vestibuli, the basilar membrane moves toward the scala tympani and the round window moves outward.

Attached to the basilar membrane is the organ of Corti, a highly organized collection of hair cells, supporting cells, and neural elements. Three rows of outer hair cells are separated from one row of

* A good source for detailed illustrations of the cat cochlea is Retzius' classic work (1884).

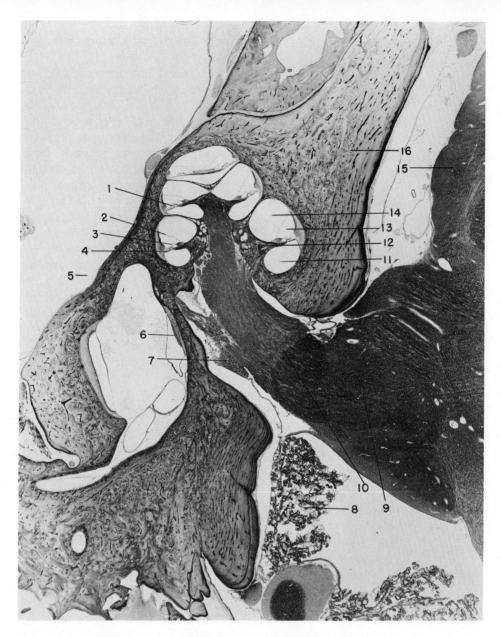

Figure 3.1   A horizontal cross section of a cat's left cochlea, auditory nerve, and cochlear nucleus.

The section is oriented so that the top of the cat would be at the bottom of the figure. The numbered structures are labeled as follows:

1. Organ of Corti
2. Reissner's membrane
3. Tectorial membrane
4. Basilar membrane
5. Middle-ear cavity
6. Macula of the saccule
7. Ganglion of Scarpa
8. Choroid plexus
9. Cochlear nucleus
10. Schwann sheath–glial junction
11. Scala tympani
12. Spiral ganglion in modiolus
13. Scala media
14. Scala vestibuli
15. Medulla oblongata
16. Temporal bone

inner hair cells by pillar cells. The hair cells are specialized receptor cells that receive at their bases the peripheral endings not only of the spiral ganglion cells but also of efferent fibers to the cochlea. The cell bodies or somas of the spiral ganglion cells lie in a bony core, the modiolus of the cochlea, and exhibit two processes (Lorente de Nó, 1933, 1937), one extending peripherally to the organ of Corti, the other extending centrally to the cochlear nucleus of the medulla. Both the peripheral and central extensions are axonal in structure and are usually considered parts of the auditory nerve.

Our recordings are all taken from the axons central to the ganglion; these axons are homologous to the central extensions of somatosensory neurons which form the dorsal roots of the spinal cord. The central extensions of the spiral ganglion cells in the internal auditory meatus are covered by Schwann sheath cells up to the point where they reach the interstitial nucleus of the cochlear nucleus and become associated with neuroglial elements. We have never seen cell bodies of neurons between the spiral ganglion and the glia–Schwann sheath junction. Suggestions that cell bodies of neurons are present in the nerve (Galambos and Davis, 1948; Harrison and Warr, 1962) are usually based on the finding of cell bodies central to the glia–Schwann sheath junction.

The number of fibers in the cat's auditory nerve has been estimated at approximately 50,000 (Gacek and Rasmussen, 1961). These fibers have a unimodal distribution of diameters with almost all of the fiber diameters falling between 2 and 6μ. The fibers in the main trunk of the nerve are myelinated and have a Schwann sheath covering even over the cell somas in the spiral ganglion (Held, 1926). Unmyelinated fibers, possibly of the autonomic system, also exist in the auditory nerve and spiral ganglion (Rosenbluth, 1962; Engström, Ades, and Hawkins, 1965). There are, of course, efferent fibers to the cochlea (Rasmussen, 1960), whose single-unit responses have been studied recently by Fex (1962). At the central end of the internal auditory meatus these efferent fibers run in the vestibular part of the eighth nerve. The small number of efferent fibers and the long latency of their responses suggest that the efferent fibers might not be of greatest interest in a first examination of stimulus coding. It is also possible that activity in the efferent fibers is drastically reduced by anesthesia.

In contrast to the relatively simple description of the fibers in the main trunk of the auditory nerve, the description of fibers and their endings at either the peripheral end in the cochlea or at the central end in the cochlear nucleus is extremely complicated. The innervation of the cochlea has been described for a number of different species (Retzius, 1884; Ramón y Cajal, 1909–1911; Held, 1926; Lorente de Nó, 1937; Polyak, McHugh, and Judd, 1946; Fernandez, 1951). The peripheral portion contains at least two main types of fibers, the radial and the spiral. Statistics are not available on the number and distribution of these fiber types, but it is usually said that (1) the innervation of inner hair cells is predominantly by radial fibers that end on only a few cells; (2) the innervation of outer hair cells is partially by radial fibers that go to a few cells and partially by spiral fibers that may run along as much as a third of a cochlear turn, innervating many cells; and (3) each spiral fiber thus supplies many hair cells, and each hair cell is connected to several fibers, radial or spiral. Electron microscope studies have given some information about the nerve endings in the cochlea but have not yet provided generally accepted descriptions of the detailed relation of fibers to endings (Engström and Wersäll, 1958; Iurato, 1961; Smith, 1961; Smith and Sjöstrand, 1961; Engström, Ades, and Hawkins, 1965). Many of the endings in the cochlea have been shown to be of efferent origin (Iurato, 1962; Kimura and Wersäll, 1962; Smith and Rasmussen, 1963; Spoendlin and Gacek, 1963; Engström, Ades, and Hawkins, 1965).

The central extensions of the auditory nerve fibers (or primary fibers) have been studied by a number of scientists using classical anatomical techniques (Ramón y Cajal, 1909–1911; Lorente de Nó, 1933; Lewy and Kobrak, 1936). They have found that a single auditory nerve fiber may branch to innervate hundreds of cells throughout the cochlear nucleus. The detailed descriptions of Ramón y Cajal (1909–1911) and Lorente de Nó (1937) indicate that the anatomical relations of fibers within the nucleus are orderly, but the functional significance of this order is still unknown.

3.2 Criteria for Primary Units

The chief difficulty in recording from primary auditory units is a consequence of the cat's anatomy: the length of nerve that is completely free of cells belonging to the interstitial nucleus is extremely short. Although in some species cells of this nucleus are found rather peripherally in the nerve (Contu, 1958; Harrison and Warr, 1962), this is fortunately not so in the cat. By approaching the nerve intracranially through the posterior fossa at the proper angle, one can usually avoid not only the cells of the interstitial nucleus but also the vestibular branch of the eighth nerve and the efferent bundle to the cochlea.

Nevertheless, it is essential to establish electrophysiological criteria for determining whether each unit studied is primary. Although some general electrophysiological criteria have been established for somatosensory primary fibers (Frank, 1959), it is uncertain whether these particular criteria hold for the auditory system.

In exploratory experiments on 50 cats, we found units obviously responsive to sound throughout the region where the auditory nerve enters the cochlear nucleus. However, responses from more than one unit were rarely found at a given micropipette location. Slight movements of the micropipette would either gain or lose "contact" with units as the micropipette was advanced but not as it was withdrawn. Our findings suggest that these micropipettes must be very close to a unit for spikes to become detectable.

It soon became evident that units in the general region of the nerve and nucleus could be separated into two distinct groups. When units

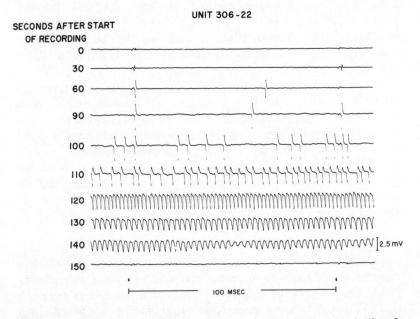

Figure 3.2 Spike recordings from a unit as a micropipette was slowly advanced through the cochlear nucleus.

The times of click presentations for all traces are indicated by the 2 dots above the time calibration. Stimuli: 10/sec clicks, −50 db. In all figures showing recordings an upward deflection indicates negativity at the recording electrode relative to the headholder.

of the first group are first contacted, usually a small (100 μV) positive-negative spike is seen. As the electrode is advanced, spike amplitude increases and the over-all discharge rate of the unit increases. With further advance of the electrode, the spike discharges become regular and occur with short interspike intervals (as short as 1 msec). As recording continues, spike duration lengthens and discharge rate decreases; abruptly the discharges cease, and only a slow wave is seen in response to clicks. This sequence of events illustrates what is called "injury" discharges that are characteristic of severely damaged units in the mammalian central nervous system (Figure 3.2). If all units had responded so drastically to the presence of the micropipette, there would have been little point in examining time patterns of discharges. Fortunately, units in the second group never show significant changes in time patterns of discharges as a result of micropipette insertion; they exhibit predominantly positive spikes with irregular time patterns of discharge (see Figures 3.3 and 8.1).

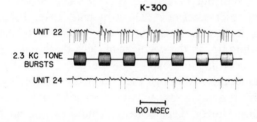

Figure 3.3 Sample spike trains from 2 auditory nerve fibers.
The middle trace shows the electric input to the earphone. The characteristic frequency (CF) of Unit 22 was 2.3 kc. CF of Unit 24: 6.6 kc. Stimuli: tone bursts, 2.3 kc, 50-msec duration, 2.5-msec rise-fall time, 10 bursts/sec, -50 db.

Although the amplitude of the spikes may change markedly as the micropipette advances, sustained injury discharges are never found.

It seems plausible to conclude that the spikes in the first group of units are recorded near dendrites or cell soma while the spikes in the second group of units are recorded near or in fibers. When a micropipette is near a dendrite-soma region, it can affect the cell's "spike generator." Fibers, on the other hand, merely transmit impulses, so it should be possible to damage a fiber severely without changing the time pattern of discharge at the spike generator.

According to this argument a unit in the first group cannot be primary because in the nerve-nucleus region the only dendrites or somas belong to cells in the cochlear nucleus. Units in the second group need not necessarily be primary fibers since fibers from cells in the interstitial nucleus will also be present in this region, although in relatively small numbers.

When we deliberately placed micropipettes in the cochlear nucleus, both groups of units were encountered. However, when the micropipettes were placed more peripherally, the proportion of units giving sustained injury discharges decreased. When the micropipettes were thrust into the nerve at an angle that carried them deeply into the internal auditory meatus, no units of the first group were encountered. Along a single micropipette track units were encountered in close succession: when contact with one unit was lost, a slight advance of the micropipette established contact with another unit. It seemed to us that the micropipette was penetrating a region densely packed with units, and we concluded that these units must be auditory nerve fibers.

We obtained supporting evidence for this conclusion by inserting a different type of microelectrode into the same nerve-nucleus region. This type of microelectrode (Dowben and Rose, 1953; Gesteland, Howland, Lettvin, and Pitts, 1959) has a 5μ ball of platinum black as the recording tip. In the cochlear nucleus these microelectrodes are capable of recording unit spike discharges, frequently from many units simultaneously. Although these microelectrodes do record injury discharges from many units, activity from some units remains recordable over large linear displacements (hundreds of microns) during both advance and withdrawal of the electrodes. Presumably these electrodes record the extracellular electric fields of discharging units. When inserted into the nerve, these electrodes do not record unit spike discharges but only slow-wave responses. It may well be that the extracellular electric fields of auditory nerve fibers are too weak and too localized to be satisfactorily recorded by such a microelectrode.

Some mention should be made of another physiological criterion for primary units, one that was suggested by Tasaki and Davis (1955) and later by Rupert, Moushegian, and Galambos (1963). If the latency of unit responses to clicks is equal to or shorter than that of the N_1 response at the round window, the unit must be primary since the N_1 response is generally interpreted to be the summed activity of auditory nerve fibers. In our study a large number of units presumed to be auditory nerve fibers showed short-latency responses, but an equally large number of units located very peripherally in the internal auditory meatus did not. Thus the latency criterion may constitute a sufficient, but not necessary, condition for classifying a unit as primary.

3.3 Tonotopic Localization in the Auditory Nerve

When we introduced tonal stimuli, it became obvious that different units responded to different ranges of frequencies. Figure 3.3 shows sample responses from two units to tone bursts of 2.3 kc. In this case Unit 22 clearly responds to the tone burst, whereas Unit 24 appears to discharge irregularly whether the acoustic stimuli are present or not. By changing the frequency and level of the tone bursts and observing the responses on a monitor oscilloscope, one may determine the combination of values over which each unit is responsive. A response area is an area on a graph of stimulus intensity versus frequency that contains all intensities and frequencies capable of producing a detectable response (Galambos and Davis, 1943). The outline of the response area is called the "tuning curve," and the frequency to which a unit is most sensitive — the tip of the tuning curve — is called the characteristic frequency (CF).

One of our first findings was that single units exhibit discharges in spite of diligent attempts to reduce extraneous acoustic stimuli. We shall reserve the term "spontaneous activity" for discharges that are present in the absence of any controlled or measurable acoustic stimuli. We cannot, however, use the term spontaneous activity to characterize the spikes in Figure 3.3 since a controlled acoustic stimulus was presented repetitively. Those spikes that do not appear to be time-locked to stimulus presentations will be represented by the term "baseline activity." Spikes that are demonstrably time-locked to stimulus presentations will be called "responses." Thus Unit 22 in Figure 3.3 shows both baseline activity and responses, while Unit 24 shows only baseline activity. Obviously as stimulus repetition rate decreases, the distinction between baseline activity and spontaneous activity becomes less important.

Tasaki found that primary units in the guinea pig (1954) and cat (1960) have tuning curves with nearly flat slopes on the low-frequency side. Had this finding been confirmed by our data, it would have furnished an additional criterion in classifying units as primary. However, the tuning curves for units from very peripheral locations turned out to be steeper on the low-frequency side than those of Tasaki's curves. This was especially so for units having the shortest response latencies and, therefore, having the best claim to classification as primary units.

The data for tuning curves also enabled us to obtain some knowledge of the spatial distribution of CF for single penetrations of the micropipette. Figure 3.4 shows four such examples. In some experiments the first units along a track had high CF; as the micropipette

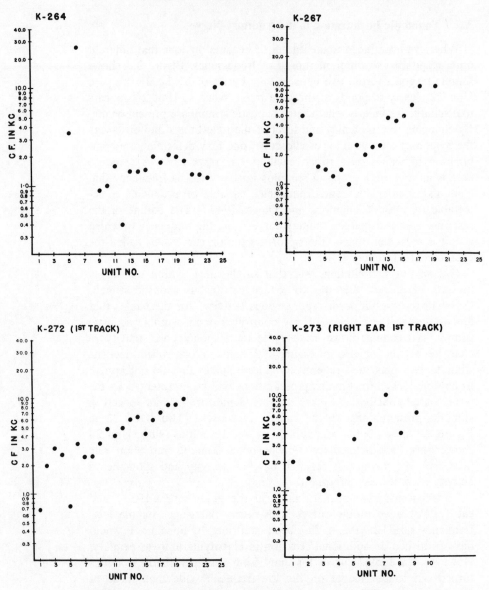

Figure 3.4 Characteristic frequencies (CF) of auditory nerve fibers from 4 different cats plotted versus unit number.

Each graph represents units obtained in a single electrode track. Unit numbers are given in the order that units are encountered. CF were not obtained for all units so that some unit numbers are not represented by points on these graphs.

advanced, the CF of units successively encountered had lower CF, and subsequent units showed higher CF (i.e., Figure 3.4, Cat 272). Almost always the last units in a track (usually just before the micro-pipette broke against bone) had high CF. Figure 3.5 shows calibrated micrometer measurements for a micropipette track. Although these measurements are not precise indicators of electrode location, active units seem to be distributed fairly uniformly along the track; there are no obvious silent regions. These facts may be explained by the anatomical arrangement of the fibers within the internal auditory meatus. Although along much of the nerve fibers from the *basal* turns of the cochlea tend to lie on the surface of the nerve, at certain locations fibers from the *apex* of the cochlea lie on the surface of the nerve (Sando, 1965).

Finally, it should be mentioned that when we inserted microelec-trodes into what seemed to be the vestibular part of the eighth nerve, we encountered units that show large regular spike discharges in the absence of sound. These units do not respond to sound even at the highest stimulus levels used in this study. In one such instance the microelectrode was left in place and the tissue sectioned for his-tological examination: the electrode was found in the vestibular nerve.

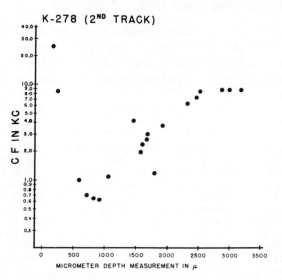

Figure 3.5 CF of units obtained in a single track plotted versus depth of electrode penetration.

Depth of penetration is represented by the calibrated readings on the micro-manipulator and are therefore only approximate.

4. Response Patterns to "Standard" Clicks

4.1 Definition of "Standard" Clicks

Because clicks are punctiform in time and evoke responses in units sensitive to frequencies throughout the audio-frequency spectrum, they were chosen as the search stimuli. In order to make experiments comparable, we specified a certain number of stimulus parameters as "standard."

Standard Clicks

Level	Polarity	Duration	Repetition Rate
(-50 db re 100-V input to the condenser earphones.) At this level, which is about 30 db above the visual detection level for N_1, almost all units exhibit visually detectable responses.	Rarefaction clicks (that is, clicks that result in an initial outward motion of the tympanic membrane).	100-μsec electric pulses. The duration of the acoustic click is illustrated in Figure 2.3.	10/sec. At a level of approximately -50 db, 10/sec is the highest rate at which effects on the amplitude of N_1 are no longer detectable (Peake, Kiang, and Goldstein, 1962).

4.2 PST Histograms of Responses to Standard Clicks

Responses to standard clicks are displayed both as raw data and PST histograms in Figure 4.1. While the N_1 recordings are relatively

20

UNIT 296-19
PST HISTOGRAM

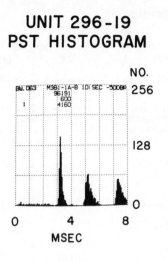

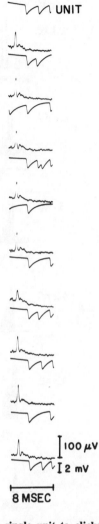

RW
UNIT

100 μV
2 mV

8 MSEC

Figure 4.1 **Time patterns of responses of a single unit to clicks displayed in a poststimulus-time histogram (PST histogram).**

The column of traces at the right shows responses to 10 successive clicks. The start of each pair of traces is synchronized with a click presentation. Upper traces show round-window responses (RW). The large upward deflection is N_1. Lower traces show spike discharges from the unit. The spikes are seen as downward deflections. The PST histogram at the left shows the distribution of the latencies of spikes during a 1-minute sample of recording. The vertical axis represents the number of spikes having a particular latency. The horizontal axis represents time after the electric pulse is delivered to the earphone. CF: 0.54 kc; stimuli: 10/sec clicks, −50 db.

PST HISTOGRAMS

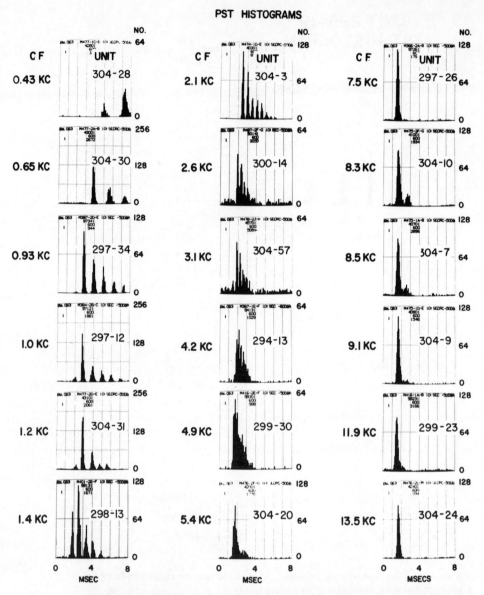

Figure 4.2   PST histograms of responses to clicks recorded from 18 units found in 6 different cats.

These units were selected to cover a wide range of CF. Histograms are arranged according to CF. Stimuli: 10/sec clicks, −50 db. (The click level for Unit 294-13 was −60 db.)

stable from click to click, the time pattern of spike discharges fluctuates considerably for identical stimuli that are well above "threshold." The PST histogram shows that on the average the spike discharges occur at preferred times with respect to the stimulus.

Figure 4.2 shows PST histograms for a representative sample of units. It is at once clear that the response pattern from different units differs considerably for standard clicks. Figure 4.2 shows also that many of the histograms exhibit a number of peaks separated by relatively constant interpeak intervals. Other histograms have essentially a single peak.

Since the insertion of a micropipette into the nerve could conceivably have altered the discharge patterns of the units, it was necessary to determine whether differences in response patterns could be accounted for by changes associated with injury. The results of a control study are illustrated in Figure 4.3. Examination of the histogram in Figure 4.3 shows no significant difference in response patterns despite very large changes in spike amplitude. As long as a spike exceeds a certain amplitude level, it is processed by the computer, and the number of spikes represented in each histogram stays substantially constant, except for the bottom histogram. When the spikes become very small, some of them are missed by the computer, although the time patterns of peaks in the histogram still remain similar.

These results may be interpreted, rather speculatively, in the following way: as the micropipette first contacts the fiber, perhaps penetrating the myelin sheath to touch the membrane (Tasaki, 1952), the spikes are large. A sudden increase in amplitude, frequently accompanied by dc shifts, probably indicates the penetration of the cell's membrane by the micropipette. Since the spikes presumably are initiated at sites remote from the micropipette, injury to the fiber by the pipette does not affect the discharge pattern sufficiently to alter the PST histograms. In short, the local criterion of the responses may diminish drastically without affecting the time pattern of the unit discharges. Thus, we may assume that our recorded discharge patterns are representative of "normal" discharge patterns.

Records from successive units contacted along a single track, often obtained within minutes of one another, may yield PST histograms with very different patterns. This observation suggests that factors such as anesthesia or trauma are insufficient explanations for the observed differences in discharge patterns.

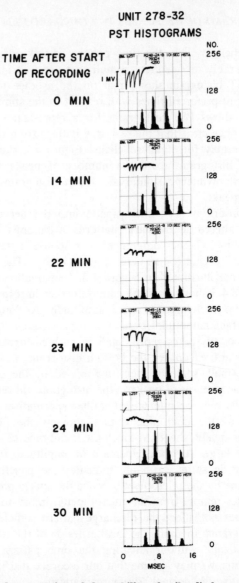

Figure 4.3 A demonstration of the stability of spike discharge patterns for a single unit over a long period of time.

PST histograms are of 1-minute samples of data taken from a 30-minute record. The insets in each histogram show 10-millisecond samples of spike discharges synchronized with click presentations. When the recordings began, spikes were more than a millivolt in amplitude but gradually decreased until at about 23 minutes after the start of recording there is an abrupt increase. Thereafter the spikes decreased in size rapidly until they were too small to trigger the computer. Some spikes were missed in the computation of the bottom histogram. CF: 0.43 kc; stimuli: 10/sec clicks, −50 db.

4.3 Relation of Single-Unit Discharge Patterns to Mechanical Events in the Cochlea

A number of consistently reproducible relations were found in comparing histograms from many units. PST histograms with single peaks seemed to be characteristic of units having the shortest latencies; these units were thus most likely to be primary. However, the latency of the first peak in PST histograms with multiple peaks may often be rather long. From the PST histograms for standard clicks, both the latency of the first peak (L) and the time between adjacent peaks (ΔP) can be measured, as illustrated in Figure 4.4. For each unit the values for L and ΔP can be related to the unit's characteristic frequency (CF).

UNIT 296-19
PST HISTOGRAM

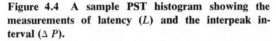

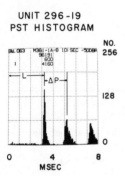

Figure 4.4 A sample PST histogram showing the measurements of latency (L) and the interpeak interval (ΔP).

Measurements are always made to the peaks of the distributions unless otherwise specified. L is measured from the onset of the electric pulse to the earphone.

The results of plotting CF against L are shown in Figure 4.5: for units with CF above 2 to 3 kc, L is short (1.3 to 1.8 msec); for units with CF below these values, L increases as CF decreases; for units with CF around 0.3 kc, L may be as long as 4 to 5 msec.

There is considerable scatter of the points in Figure 4.5, and several sources of error may contribute to this scatter: (1) there are errors involved in measuring L and in determining CF; (2) the effective stimulus level can hardly be considered equivalent for different units since their thresholds to click stimuli vary greatly; and (3) the distance between the point of spike generation and the recording site is not the same for all fibers. This difference would result in a systematic difference in conduction time of the nerve impulse to the point of recording.

Although these sources of variability may account for most of the scatter of points in Figure 4.5, they seem unable to account for the systematic change in L with CF for CF below 2 to 3 kc. A more likely interpretation can be made on the basis of Békésy's data (1960): it may be 5 msec before mechanical disturbances are apparent at the

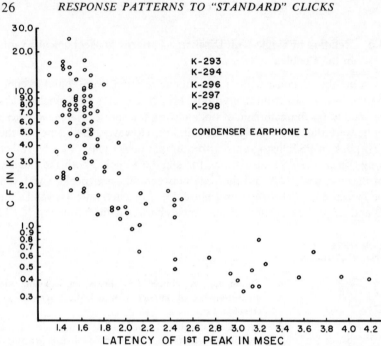

Figure 4.5   The CF for 102 units plotted against *L*, the latency of the first peak in the PST histograms, for click responses.

CF are plotted on a logarithmic scale. Stimuli: 10/sec clicks, −50 db.

apex of the cochlea. Furthermore, these disturbances travel rapidly in the basal turn and more slowly at the apex. The present physiological data show that units with CF above 2 to 3 kc respond almost synchronously, while units with lower CF respond with systematically greater *L*. Since the range of *L* covers approximately 3 msec, agreement with Békésy's data is satisfactory. Thus *L* for primary units seems to be directly related to the longitudinal position along the cochlear partition where the auditory nerve fibers terminate.

In Figure 4.6, the reciprocal of the CF, that is, the characteristic period, is plotted on a linear scale against ΔP. These two quantities are linearly related; the straight line has a slope of 1 showing that ΔP is indeed 1/CF. By extrapolation it is thus possible to predict the CF for units from the PST histogram for standard clicks, if ΔP is measurable. Data for tuning curves are tedious to obtain and subject to error in determining thresholds, whereas PST histograms for standard clicks require only one short run. Measurements of ΔP from PST histograms are thus more accurate than the determination of CF by visual or auditory inspection. In taking tuning curves, the error in making readings of frequency is greatest for low frequencies so that the scatter of points in Figure 4.6 is greatest for units with low CF. It is interesting to note that both CF and ΔP are independent of the conduction time of the nerve impulses or electrode location along the axon from which the recordings were taken.

The multiple responses of single primary units to single clicks almost certainly reflect mechanical events in the cochlea. To use an example, when a click is delivered to the ear, a given point along the basilar membrane responds by vibrating in a damped oscillatory manner with a frequency that is determined by the local mechanical characteristics of the membrane and of the fluids. Since the elasticity of the membrane changes with position along its length, one would expect the frequency of vibration also to change (Békésy, 1960). In

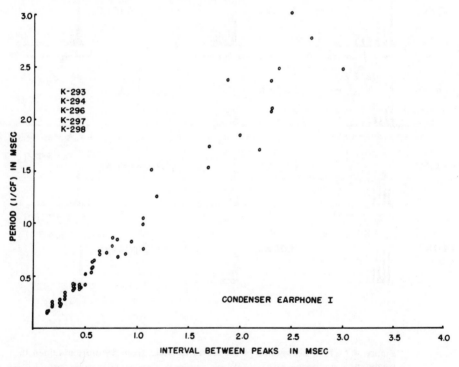

Figure 4.6 **The characteristic period for 56 of the units in Figure 4.5 plotted on a linear scale against the interpeak interval (Δ P) as measured from the PST histograms.**

(ΔP cannot be measured for units with high CF.)

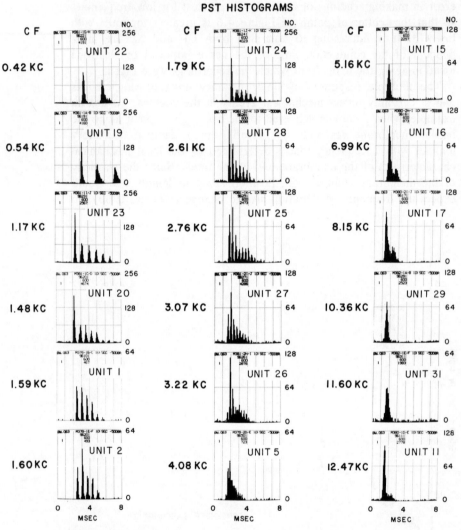

Figure 4.7 PST histograms of responses to clicks from 18 units obtained in a single cat.

The preparation was left undisturbed except when electrode position was changed. The histograms are arranged according to CF. Stimuli: 10/sec clicks, -50 db. The VDL for N_1 cat was -80 db. Compare this figure with Figure 4.2.

fact, the frequency of vibration exhibited in response to a click should correspond to the frequency of tone to which each point on the membrane is maximally sensitive. Models for the response of the basilar membrane to an impulsive stimulus (that is, a click) have been calculated by several workers (Flanagan, 1962; Siebert, 1962) using Békésy's data (1960). These models all show that each point on the basilar membrane will vibrate at a frequency that is determined by its longitudinal location along the membrane. Furthermore, in the basal turn the membrane will be set into vibration with a short latency, while in the apical turn the vibration will have a long latency. Thus the timing of peaks in PST histograms of auditory nerve fiber activity is in good agreement with both calculated and observed mechanical events in the cochlea.

The preceding arguments need not assume that the movements of the basilar membrane are the events that directly stimulate sensori-neural activity; the movements of the hair cells and other structures in the cochlear partition are extremely complex and are not known in sufficient detail to warrant speculation with regard to their precise role in the initiation of activity at sensory-receptor and neural levels.

Having established the general relation of CF to the timing of peaks, one must face the question of whether minor differences in PST histograms for standard clicks are attributable to minor differences in effective stimulation, variability among cats, and so forth. To answer this question, data from units covering a wide range of CF were obtained from single cats. Figure 4.7 shows a set of results obtained from a single animal. These histograms can be compared with those of Figure 4.2, which represent data from many animals. Not only are the histograms of Figures 4.2 and 4.7 similar in general appearance, but certain details recur: for example, a second peak is seen in the histograms for units with CF near 8 kc. Its origin is unknown but may result from repetitive discharges that occur once the unit has recovered sufficiently from the previous discharge.

4.4 Responses of Units with High CF and Round-Window Neural Potentials

The PST histograms of units with high CF's show only a single peak. This peak is not easily resolvable into separate narrower peaks by computing the histograms at greater time resolutions (Figure 4.8). The coalescence of multiple peaks probably reflects an approaching limitation of the ability of either the sensory receptors or of the neural structures to follow cochlear mechanical events at high fre-

UNIT 296-15
PST HISTOGRAMS

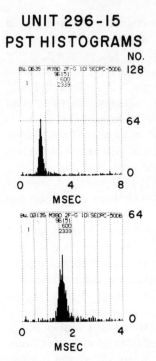

Figure 4.8 PST histograms of responses to standard clicks for a unit with high CF.

The upper histogram is run at the standard time resolution; the lower histogram is run at twice the standard resolution. The CF of the unit is 5.16 kc, so that the characteristic period for this unit should be 0.19 msec. There are no obvious peaks separated by 0.19 msec in the histogram. The upper-frequency limit of the recording system was extended to 10 kc in this experiment.

quencies. The latency of the peak in histograms from units with high CF is the same as that of the N_1 peak recorded by an electrode at the same location in the internal auditory meatus. The N_1 potential recorded in the meatus has a latency that is 0.2 msec later than the N_1 recorded at the round window. This difference in latency presumably reflects the neural conduction time from peripheral parts of the auditory nerve to more central locations.

The relation of N_1 and N_2 potentials to unit spikes can be seen in Figure 4.9 which shows the PST histograms of click responses from four representative units obtained in one cat. Superposed over the histograms are averages of the neural potentials (N_1 and N_2) that were recorded at the same time near the round window. Even considering that the latencies for units with high CF are approximately 0.2 msec longer than that of N_1 recorded from the round window, it would appear that only units with high CF contribute significantly to N_1. The responses of units with low CF not only have too long a latency, they are also too asynchronous to contribute effectively. Thus N_1 in response to clicks may give information about the activity of units that innervate the basal turn, but it can give little information about the activity of units that innervate more apical parts of the cochlea (Teas, Eldredge, and Davis, 1962).

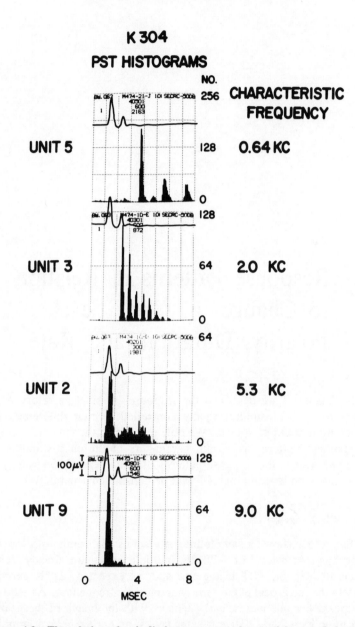

Figure 4.9 The relation of unit discharges to neural potentials recorded at the round window.

PST histograms for 4 units with different CF's are shown with the corresponding averaged round-window recordings. One-minute samples were used in all cases except in the histogram for Unit 2, where a 30-second sample was used. Stimuli: 10/sec clicks, −50 db.

5. Response Patterns in Relation to Changes in Click Level, Polarity, Duration, and Rate

In Chapter 4 we described the responses of single auditory nerve fibers to a click stimulus rigidly controlled so that differences between units could be studied. We now proceed to the study of changes in response patterns as certain parameters of the click stimulus are changed. (Since the response patterns of units depend so strongly on CF, units with low and high CF will be considered separately.)

5.1 Click Level

Figure 5.1 shows a sample intensity series for a unit with low CF (650 cps). At a level of −70 db, multiple peaks are already clearly discernible in the PST histogram, and, as expected, ΔP is approximately the reciprocal of CF (the characteristic frequency). At −60 db, the peaks become more clearly defined, with the height of the peak at 3.5 msec increased relative to later peaks; an earlier peak at approximately 2.5 msec is barely detectable. From −50 db to −20 db, the peak at 2.5 msec grows relative to later peaks until, at −30 db and −20 db, it becomes the largest peak. Throughout this range of stimulus levels each peak stays rather constant in latency. Figure 5.2 plots

32

UNIT 278-7
PST HISTOGRAMS

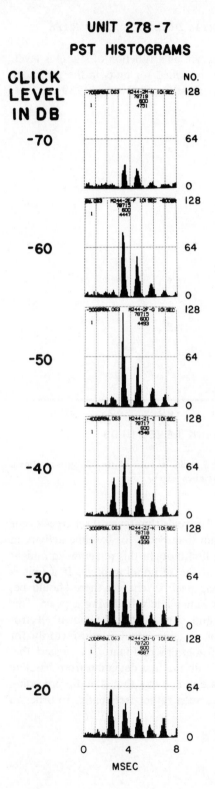

CLICK LEVEL IN DB

- -70
- -60
- -50
- -40
- -30
- -20

NO.

- 128
- 64
- 0

MSEC

Figure 5.1 Responses of a unit with a CF of 0.65 kc to clicks as a function of click level.

Stimuli: 10/sec clicks. Reference level was 4 V into dynamic earphone I.

the latencies of peaks in the histogram as a function of stimulus level. Similar multiple peaks have been described for units in the accessory superior olive (Galambos, Schwartzkopff, and Rupert, 1959).

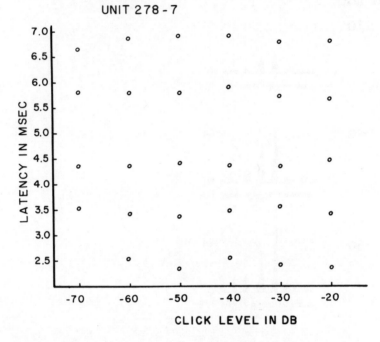

Figure 5.2   The latencies of the first 5 peaks in each of the histograms shown in Figure 5.1 plotted as a function of click level.

Close examination of Figure 5.1 reveals that fewer discharges occur between the peaks of the histogram than occur for baseline activity in a corresponding time interval. At first thought this phenomenon might be attributable to refractoriness of the responding units. If a unit is refractory for some time following each discharge, there should be, on the average, fewer discharges immediately following a peak. This explanation, although plausible and consistent with known electro-physiological principles, does not seem to account satisfactorily for all aspects of the findings. The histograms of Figure 5.1 suggest that at click levels of −70 db and −60 db the first deviation from baseline activity may be an average decrease in activity, that is, a dip preceding the first peak; such histograms are seen rather frequently. In order to investigate this point, intensity series were obtained in 1-db rather than 10-db steps.

To obtain decisive results, we had to meet several conditions: (1) The unit had to have a low CF so that multiple peaks would be present in the PST histogram. (2) The unit also had to have a fairly high rate of spontaneous activity so that decreases in baseline activity could be more easily substantiated. (3) Records had to be obtained at many closely spaced click levels; preferably these levels should be low in order to minimize the effects of refractoriness (Peake, Kiang, and Goldstein, 1962).

Figure 5.3 shows one fortunate example. The high rate of spontaneous activity of this unit made it difficult to determine a click threshold accurately; the best visual determination of the threshold was −85 db. As shown by the computed PST histograms, a clear response (that is, significant time-locked deviation from baseline activity) is present at −95 db. Note that even at the lowest stimulus levels there seem to be multiple peaks* with reduction of baseline activity between peaks. Note also that for histograms obtained at click levels of −88, −86, −85, −82, −81, −77, and −76 db, the initial deviation from the average level of baseline activity is clearly a decrease in activity. It is difficult to see how refractoriness can account for this initial decrease. On the basis of current knowledge of cochlear mechanics, it seems more reasonable to interpret alternate dips and peaks in the histograms as follows: Deflection of the cochlear partition in one direction results in enhanced neural activity, and deflection in the opposite direction results in a diminution of neural activity in comparison with the unit's level of baseline activity. Figure 5.4 shows that there are no significant shifts in the latencies of the peaks.

From the PST histograms it is possible to derive another set of numbers that may be of functional significance. Consider, for example, the two units whose histograms are shown in Figures 5.1 and 5.7. Figure 5.5 plots both the rate of time-locked activity and total (time-locked plus baseline) activity as functions of click level.

Unit 264-19 has so little spontaneous activity that the rate of time-locked spike activity is almost equivalent to the rate of total spike activity. For Unit 278-7, there is little change in total activity although the rate of time-locked spike activity increases with click level, as in the case of Unit 264-19.

* The existence of multiple peaks in the PST histogram does not necessarily imply the presence of repetitive discharges to each click.

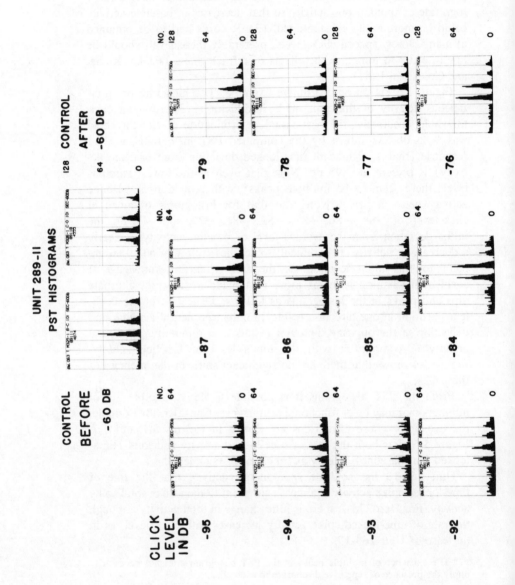

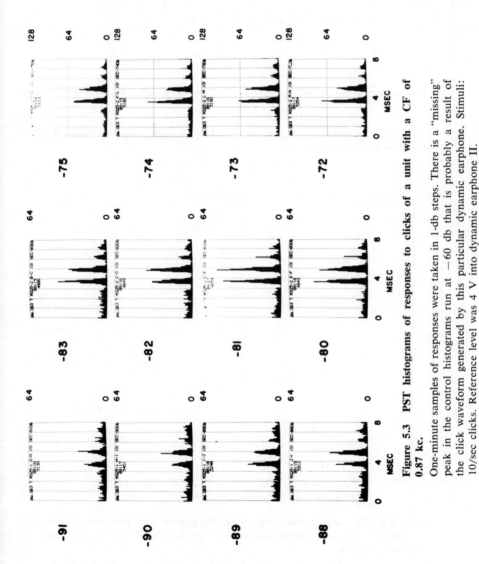

Figure 5.3   PST histograms of responses to clicks of a unit with a CF of 0.87 kc.

One-minute samples of responses were taken in 1-db steps. There is a "missing" peak in the control histograms run at −60 db that is probably a result of the click waveform generated by this particular dynamic earphone. Stimuli: 10/sec clicks. Reference level was 4 V into dynamic earphone II.

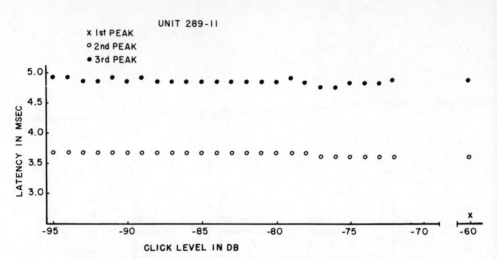

UNIT 289-11

x 1st PEAK
o 2nd PEAK
● 3rd PEAK

Figure 5.4 Latencies of the peaks in the PST histograms shown in Figure 5.3 plotted against click level.

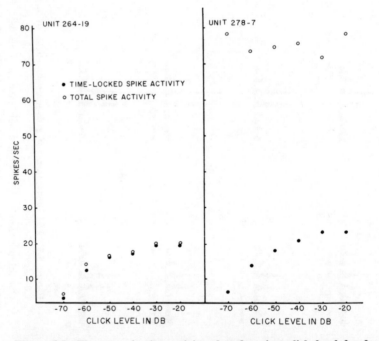

Figure 5.5 The rate of spike activity plotted against click level for 2 units, one (264-19) with low spontaneous activity and the other (278-7) with high spontaneous activity.

The time-locked spike activity was obtained by summing the number of responses represented in the peaks of the PST histograms and dividing by 60 (the number of seconds represented by each histogram). The total spike activity was obtained by counting the number of spikes over the same 1-minute sample and dividing by 60. CF Unit 264-19: 2.0 kc; CF Unit 278-7: 0.65 kc. The sound source was dynamic earphone I. Reference level for Unit 264-19 was 2.5 V, but it was 4 V for Unit 278-7.

Similar functions are plotted for the other units in Figure 5.6. The rate of time-locked spike activity appears to be a monotonically increasing function of click level although there is some variation in the exact shape of the function for different units. Since the responses to clicks are packaged differently for units with high and low CF, there may be some objection to comparing click intensity functions in detail without considering CF. However, the smooth monotonic intensity functions suggest that some aspects of intensity information may be represented in the probability of time-locked spike activity. Presumably the time-locked spikes will summate when a number of primary units converge on a cell in the cochlear nucleus. At best, the functions

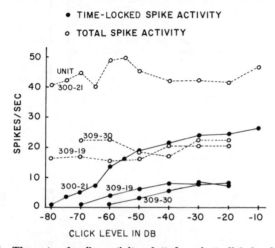

Figure 5.6 **The rate of spike activity plotted against click level for 3 units.** CF Unit 300-21: 0.47 kc; CF Unit 309-30: 2.74 kc; and CF Unit 309-19: 6.1 kc. Although the curve showing time-locked spike activity plotted against click level for Unit 300-21 is very similar to the curves for time-locked spike activity in Figure 5.4, the curves for Unit 309-19 and Unit 309-30 are not. However, all the curves for time-locked spike activity show an increase with click level to a plateau at high click levels. Reference level was 100 V into condenser earphones.

shown in Figures 5.5 and 5.6 represent only one possible set of cues for intensity changes at the level of single primary units.

5.2 Click Polarity

If increases and decreases in neural activity do result from motion of cochlear structures in opposite directions, reversal of click polarity should provide supporting evidence. Figures 5.7 to 5.11 show intensity series for both condensation and rarefaction clicks. The peaks

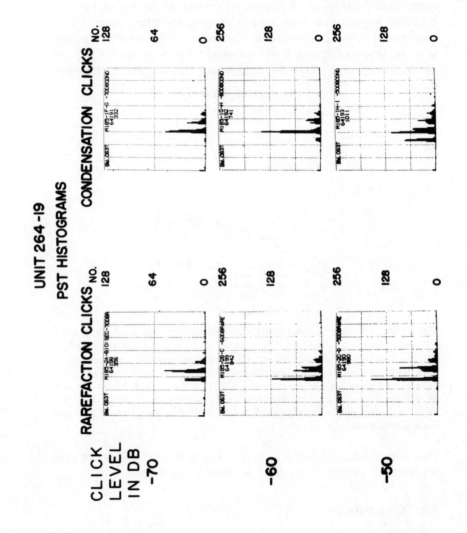

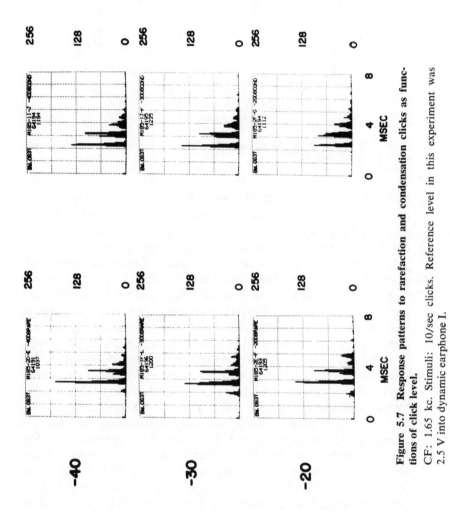

Figure 5.7 Response patterns to rarefaction and condensation clicks as functions of click level.

CF: 1.65 kc. Stimuli: 10/sec clicks. Reference level in this experiment was 2.5 V into dynamic earphone I.

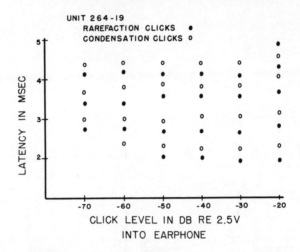

Figure 5.8   Latencies of the peaks in the PST histograms shown in Figure 5.5 plotted against click level.

for condensation clicks fall, in general, between the peaks for rarefaction clicks; that is, the peaks indicating increased activity with one polarity of click are found at approximately the times of the dips in the PST histogram that reflect decreased activity for the opposite polarity of clicks. The interleaving of peaks for condensation and rarefaction clicks, as shown in Figures 5.8 and 5.11, lends strong support to the idea that increased and decreased neural activity can result from opposite directions of movements of cochlear structures. Since at high click levels the earliest peak always occurs for rarefaction clicks, it is likely to be the rarefaction phase (in which the stapes is pulled out of the oval window) of the cochlear motion that corresponds to increased neural activity. This conclusion is in agreement with suggestions from earlier experiments with gross potentials (Rosenblith and Rosenzweig, 1952; Peake and Kiang, 1962).

A somewhat different attempt was made to determine the direction of motion that corresponds to peaks in the PST histograms by using low-level clicks. Our thought was that the polarity of clicks that are capable of eliciting responses at the lowest stimulus level would correspond to the phase of motion that triggers spike activity. Figure 5.12 yields particularly appropriate data because the click levels were in the correct range, the rate of spontaneous activity was low, and the unit's CF was low. Surprisingly, the thresholds for detecting responses in the PST histograms are virtually identical for both rarefaction and condensation clicks. Note, however, the differences in the time patterns of responses. The rarefaction clicks produce a single large peak flanked by two smaller peaks; the condensation clicks, on the other hand, produce two peaks of approximately equal size. Such differences in PST patterns may well be accounted for by the mechanical responses to the two polarities of clicks (Flanagan, 1962; Siebert, 1962).

Units with high CF are of special interest since N_1 has already been studied as a function of click polarity and intensity (Peake and Kiang, 1962). Figures 5.13 and 5.14 compare response patterns for two units with the parallel averaged round-window recordings. With increasing click level, N_1 shows a decrease in latency (up to 1 msec). The latency shifts of N_1 are accompanied by latency shifts in the peaks of the histograms for unit responses. Furthermore, as in Figure 5.14, changes in the waveforms of the gross potentials are frequently strikingly similar to changes in the pattern of histograms. These findings indicate that N_1 may indeed be the summed discharges of high-CF units although the responses from various units may be weighted differently in their contributions to N_1. At high click levels the units tend to show repetitive responses that do not correlate with CF.

5.3 Click Duration

Since many aspects of unit responses to clicks depend strongly upon CF and since click duration has a well-known effect on the distribution of stimulus energy throughout the frequency range, it seemed desirable to obtain some appreciation of the effects of changing click duration.

The energy-density spectrum of an ideal 100-μsec pulse has its first zero at 10 kc. If we assume that the earphone has no significant harmonic distortion, the energy density of the acoustic clicks is also zero at 10 kc. Hence, it is not surprising that units with CF near 10 kc almost always have high thresholds for 100-μsec clicks since there is so little stimulus energy near 10 kc. Figure 5.15 demonstrates that the threshold of a unit with CF near 10 kc rises significantly when the click duration approaches 100 μsec while the threshold of a unit with lower CF seems unaffected.

Occasionally one finds statements in the literature that certain auditory units do not respond to clicks but will respond to some other acoustic stimuli. It seems prudent to withhold speculation on the functional significance of units having such presumed characteristics until the acoustic signals have been carefully analyzed and stimulus parameters varied over a wide range of values.

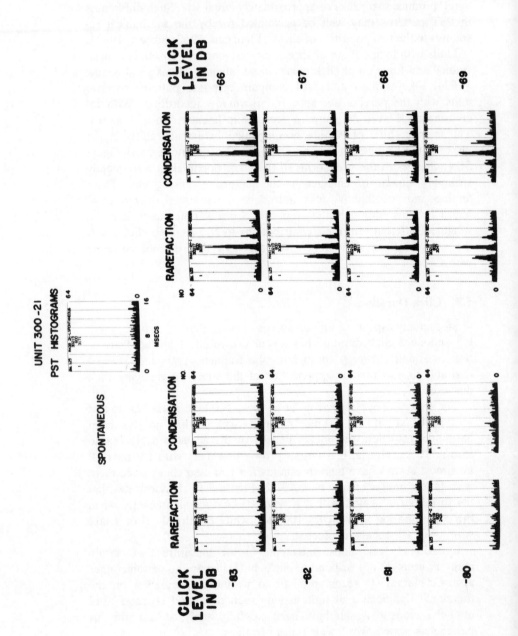

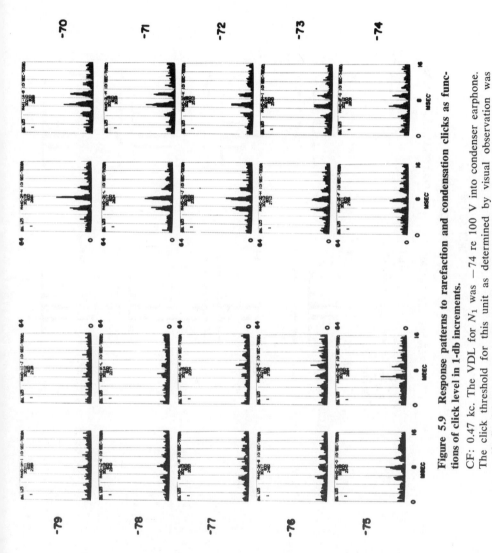

Figure 5.9 Response patterns to rarefaction and condensation clicks as functions of click level in 1-db increments.

CF: 0.47 kc. The VDL for N_1 was −74 re 100 V into condenser earphone. The click threshold for this unit as determined by visual observation was −68 db. Stimuli: 10/sec clicks. Spontaneous discharge rate: 52.5 spikes/sec.

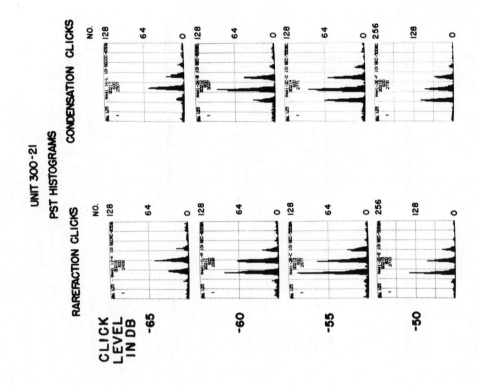

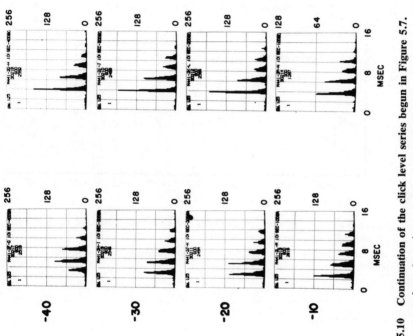

Figure 5.10 Continuation of the click level series begun in Figure 5.7. The increments have been increased to 5 and 10 db. Stimuli: 10/sec clicks.

UNIT 300-21

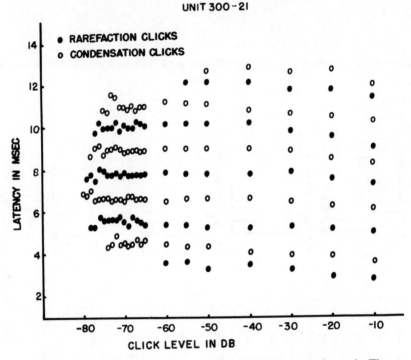

Figure 5.11 Latencies of the peaks in the PST histograms shown in Figures 5.7 and 5.8 plotted against click level.

The latency shifts at the higher click levels are the greatest that were encountered in this study.

5.4 Click Rates

The representation of stimulus rate has long been a key issue in the study of auditory neural mechanisms. Indeed, the interest in volley theories was a direct result of the discovery that the compound action potential of the auditory nerve seemed to follow frequencies of stimulation up to several thousand per second (Wever, 1949). These gross potentials have recently been studied as a function of click rate (Peake, Goldstein, and Kiang, 1962). Neural events time-locked to the delivery of clicks were found even at rates of a few thousand clicks per second. With the information provided by the preceding chapters, it is now possible to examine changes in response patterns of primary units as a function of click rate.

Figure 5.16 shows PST histograms of responses from a low-CF unit to clicks presented at different rates. The basic configuration of the histogram does not change substantially until the responses to successive clicks begin to overlap; this occurs at a rate of 200 clicks/ sec. At higher rates the responses to consecutive clicks interact in complicated, but reproducible, ways. Figure 5.17 shows that the latency of the peaks in the histograms appears to be constant as click rate changes; however, the relative heights of the individual peaks do change as a function of click rate. The first peak in the histogram is the one most affected, presumably because of its temporal proximity to responses evoked by the preceding clicks.

The duration of the entire response configuration in the PST histogram is shorter for units with high CF than that for units with low CF; hence the problem of overlapping responses begins only at higher click rates. Figure 5.18 shows that individual time-locked peaks are seen even at 1000 clicks/sec and the latencies of these peaks do not change significantly for rates up to 200 clicks/sec. However, at higher rates the latency decreases by 0.1 to 0.2 msec. Comparable decreases in latency are found in N_1 responses to clicks.

The absence of latency shifts as click rate increases up to several hundred clicks per second is consistent with the view that the responses of primary units are closely tied to mechanical events in the cochlea. We would not expect the latencies of mechanical events to change with stimulus rate, but the neural responses might well have been drastically affected. However, in the rate series shown in Figure 5.18 taken at moderate click intensities, the maximum rate of discharge of the units is approximately 100/sec. If the absolute refractory period of these neurons is taken to be 1 msec, then the units are discharging at a rate that is still low relative to their theoretical limit of 1000/sec. Perhaps larger shifts in latency would appear if some means could be found to stimulate the units and study responses at rates higher than 100/sec.

Although PST histograms are useful in examining some aspects of the responses time-locked to the stimulus, they do not give an adequate picture of a unit's over-all activity. Figure 5.19 shows interspike-interval histograms for Unit 309-27, computed from the data of Figure 2.3. The interval histogram for the spontaneous activity rises quickly to a modal value at around 4 msec and then gradually decays. In the presence of click stimulation the peak near 2 msec in each interval histogram represents intervals between successive spikes where there are multiple discharges in response to individual clicks. At higher

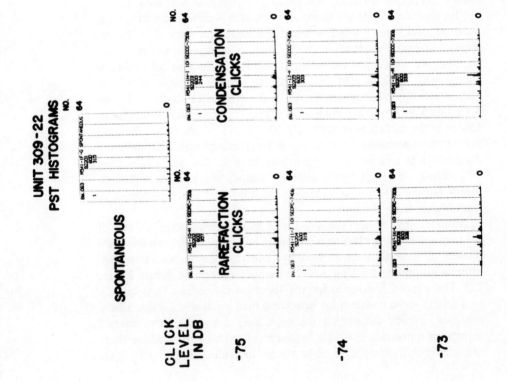

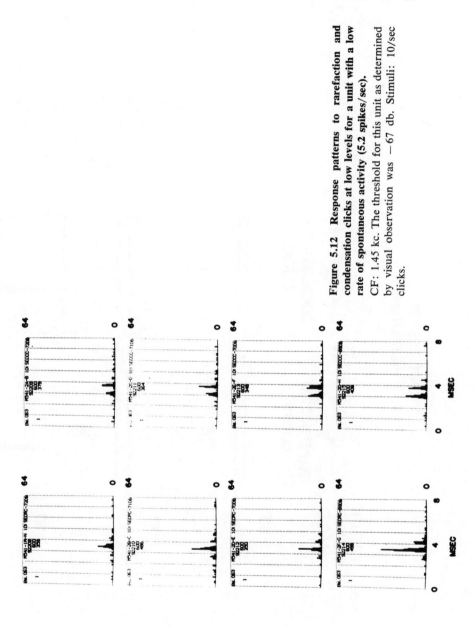

Figure 5.12 Response patterns to rarefaction and condensation clicks at low levels for a unit with a low rate of spontaneous activity (5.2 spikes/sec). CF: 1.45 kc. The threshold for this unit as determined by visual observation was −67 db. Stimuli: 10/sec clicks.

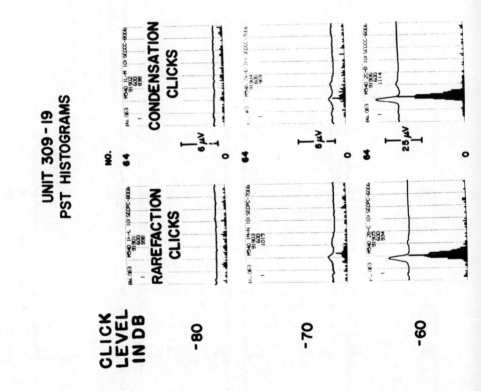

UNIT 309-19
PST HISTOGRAMS

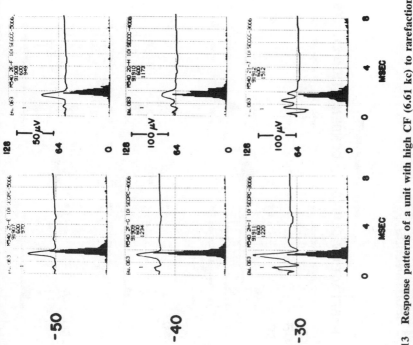

Figure 5.13   Response patterns of a unit with high CF (6.61 kc) to rarefaction and condensation clicks as a function of click level.

Superposed on the histograms are the corresponding averaged round-window responses. The early (<1-msec latency) events in the round-window records are cochlear microphonic potentials. Stimuli: 10/sec clicks.

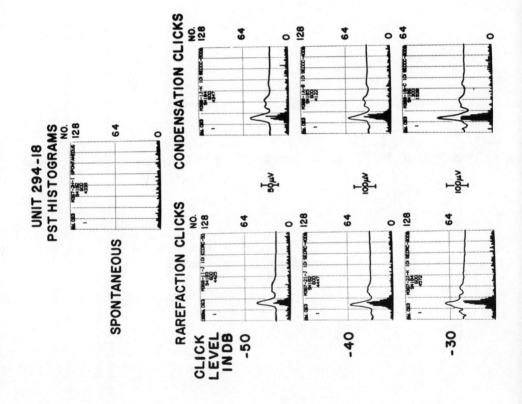

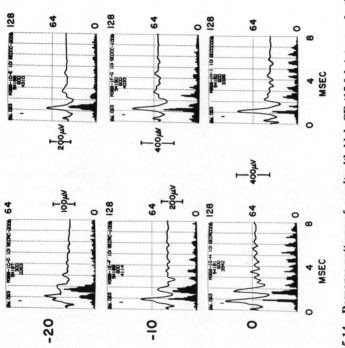

Figure 5.14 Response patterns of a unit with high CF (15.0 kc) to rarefaction and condensation clicks as a function of click level.

Superposed on the histograms are the corresponding averaged round-window responses. Stimuli: 10/sec clicks.

click rates the interval histogram shows peaks that correspond to the interclick interval and its multiples. Thus, at 20 clicks/sec, a small peak is seen at 50 msec corresponding to the interval between clicks. Units with high CF do not show the peak in the interval histogram that corresponds to multiple discharges to a single click but otherwise behave rather similarly to low-CF units (Figure 5.20).

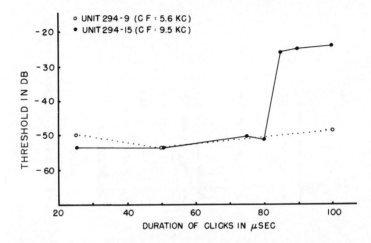

Figure 5.15. The effect of changing click duration on the visually determined threshold of 2 units, one with a CF near 10 kc and one with a much lower CF. As click duration increases, the first zero in the power spectrum appears at lower frequencies. For a 100-μsec/click the first zero is at 10 kc. Stimuli: 10/sec clicks.

If one ignores the *time patterns* of the discharges and considers only the *rate* of spike activity as click rate changes, the curves of Figures 5.21 and 5.22 are relevant. The curves are all essentially monotonic until responses to successive clicks overlap in the PST histogram. Since there are dips as well as peaks in the PST histograms for low CF units, the effects of overlap must be complicated. As overlap occurs, the over-all discharge rate might well depend upon the exact timing of the clicks and the CF of the unit.

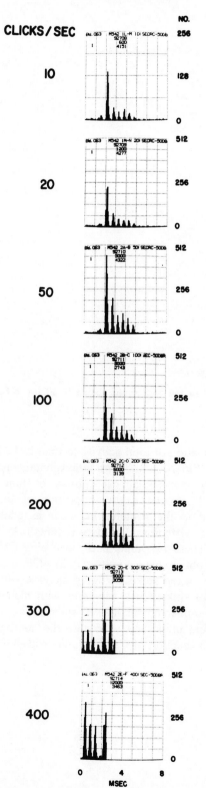

Figure 5.16 Response patterns of a unit with a CF of 1.88 kc as a function of click rate.

At click rates above 200/sec, the effects of successive clicks overlap. Length of run: 1 minute for click rates of 10, 20, and 50/sec, and 30 seconds for other click rates. Stimuli: clicks, −50 db.

UNIT 309-27

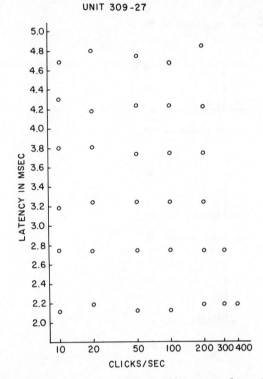

Figure 5.17   Latencies of the peaks in the histograms shown in Figure 5.16 plotted against click rate.

It is possible to examine the relation of total activity to time-locked activity (Figure 5.23). For Unit 306-20, a unit with little spontaneous activity, the total spike activity consists almost entirely of time-locked activity. For Unit 299-22, however, the proportion of the total activity that is time-locked to the stimulus increases as click rate increases. At 200 clicks/sec, virtually all activity is time-locked to the stimulus for both units. These two units both have high CF, but virtually identical curves are obtainable for units with low CF.

Although the number of time-locked spikes/sec may increase with higher click rates, the number of spikes/click decreases with higher click rates (Figure 5.24). The number of time-locked spikes/click at low click rates differs for different units largely because the number of peaks in a PST histogram is a function of CF. For units with high

CF (that is, 299-22 and 306-20), the curves relating number of time-locked spikes/click to rate resemble the curves of N_1 amplitude versus click rate (Peake, Goldstein, and Kiang 1962).

It would seem that stimulus rate can have more than a single correlate at the neural level. The many different response characteristics that change with stimulus rate may each be functionally significant for any number of specific behavioral discriminations.

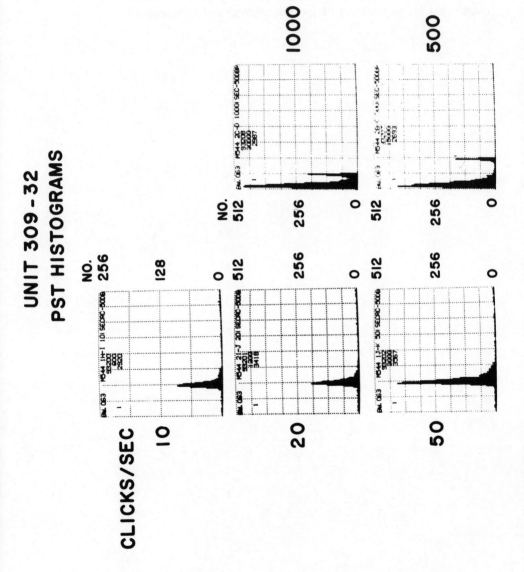

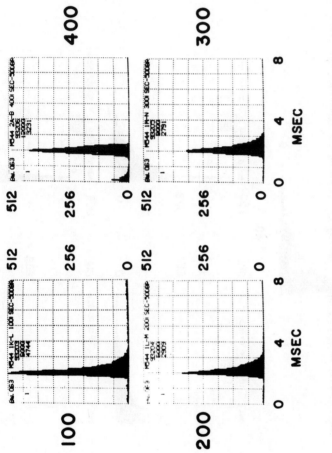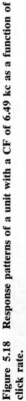

Figure 5.18   Response patterns of a unit with a CF of 6.49 kc as a function of click rate.

At click rates above 400/sec, the effects of successive clicks overlap. Length of run: 1 minute for click rates 10, 20, 50, and 100, and 30 seconds for the other click rates. Stimuli: clicks, −50 db.

UNIT 309-27
INTERVAL HISTOGRAMS

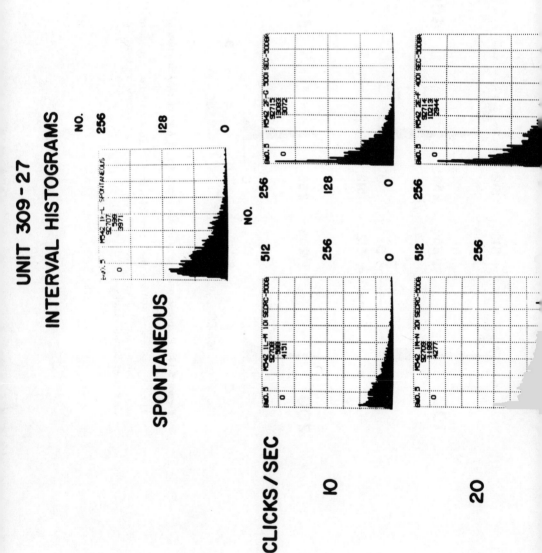

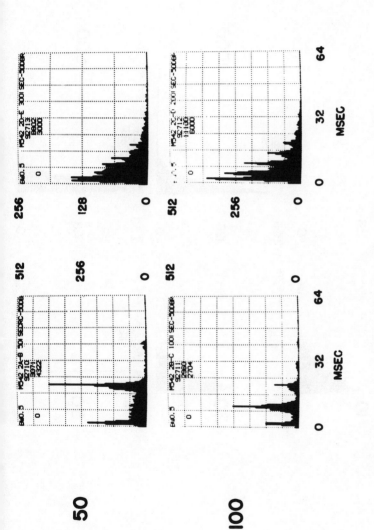

Figure 5.19 Interval histograms of spike activity of a unit with a CF of 1.88 kc as a function of click rate.

Compare with Figure 5.16. Length of run: 1 minute for spontaneous and click rates 10, 20, 50, 200/sec, and 26 seconds for other click rates. Stimuli: clicks, −50 db.

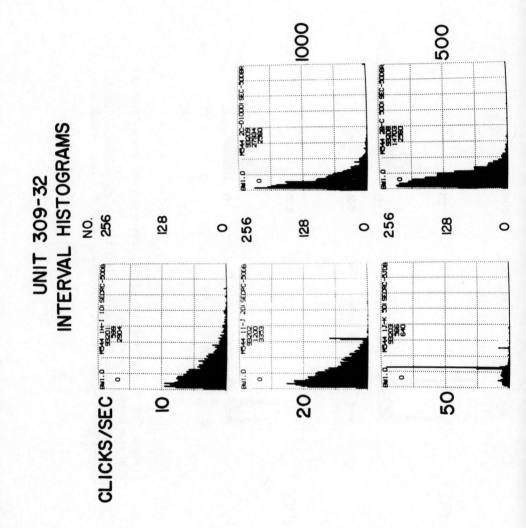

UNIT 309-32
INTERVAL HISTOGRAMS

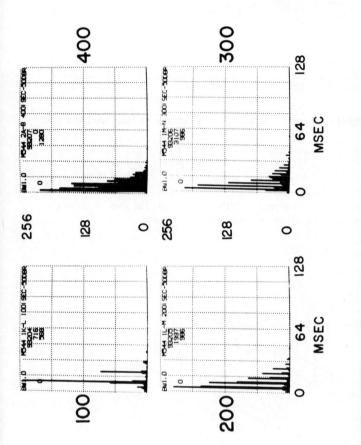

Figure 5.20 Interval histograms of spike activity of a unit with CF of 6.49 as a function of click rate.

Compare with Figure 5.18. Length of run: 1 minute for click rates 10 and 20/sec, 30 seconds for click rates 400, 500, and 1000/sec, and approximately 10 seconds for click rates 50, 100, 200, and 300/sec. Stimuli: clicks, −50 db.

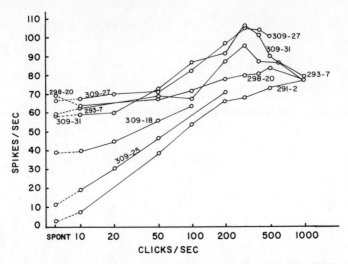

Figure 5.21 Spikes/sec versus clicks/sec for a number of units with low CF.

Unit	CF	Unit	CF
291-2	0.860 kc	309-25	1.92 kc
293-7	2.35 kc	309-27	1.88 kc
298-20	3.67 kc	309-31	0.39 kc
309-18	1.42 kc		

The points plotted as spontaneous (SPONT) represent the rate of spike discharge in the absence of clicks. Stimuli: clicks, −50 db.

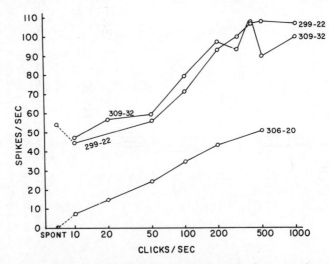

Figure 5.22 Rate of spike plotted against click rate for a number of units with high CF.

Unit	CF
299-22	8.90 kc
306-20	7.26 kc
309-32	6.49 kc

The points plotted as spontaneous (SPONT) represent the rate of spike discharges in the absence of clicks. The click level for Units 299-22 and 309-32 was −50 db. The click level for Unit 306-20 was −20 db since Unit 306-20 did not respond to clicks at −50 db.

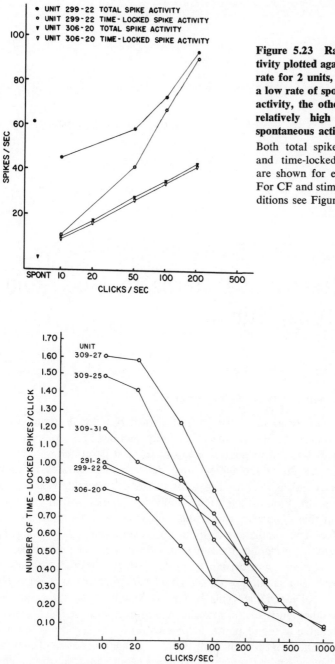

Figure 5.23 Rate of activity plotted against click rate for 2 units, one with a low rate of spontaneous activity, the other with a relatively high rate of spontaneous activity.

Both total spike activity and time-locked activity are shown for each unit. For CF and stimulus conditions see Figure 5.24.

Figure 5.24 The number of time-locked spikes/click plotted against clicks/sec.

The number of time-locked spikes were obtained by summing the spikes in the peaks of the PST histogram.

Unit	CF	Unit	CF
291-2	0.86 kc	309-25	1.92 kc
299-22	8.90 kc	309-27	1.88 kc
306-20	7.26 kc	309-31	0.39 kc

6. Response Patterns to Noise and Tonal Stimuli

6.1 Response Patterns to Tone Bursts

In the preceding chapters we have shown how tonal stimuli were used to determine the characteristic frequencies (CF) of units, but the time patterns of responses to tones were not described.

Figure 6.1 shows the typical time patterns of responses to short tone bursts for eight units. For units below approximately 5 kc, the discharges are time-locked to the individual cycles within the tone burst, but this synchrony cannot be seen with the time scale used in Figure 6.1. The histograms in Figure 6.1 were obtained by using the tone bursts at moderate intensities and slow rates. The envelopes of these histograms have certain common features: there is usually a sharp peak at the onset with a gradual "adaptation" to a relatively stable rate of discharge. This pattern is found for neural responses in many other parts of the nervous system and may, at least in part, be attributable to the response characteristics of the sensory receptors. After the tone burst is turned off, there is a sharp decrease of activity followed by a gradual return to the level of spontaneous discharges. We have seen this characteristic pattern of response to tone bursts even in unit recordings from the peripheral stump after the eighth nerve is severed in the internal auditory meatus. (See Appendix B.)

68

K-297
PST HISTOGRAMS

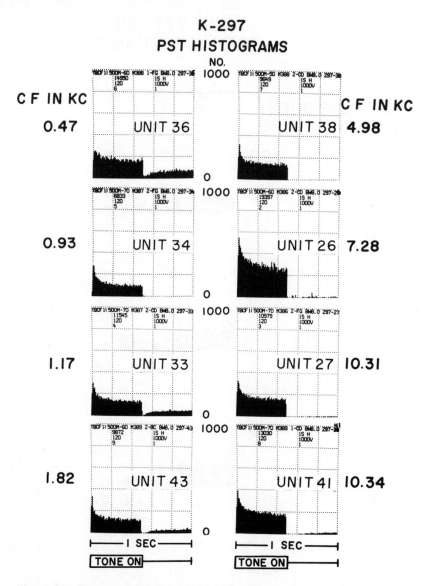

Figure 6.1 Response patterns of units to bursts of tone.

Each histogram represents 2 minutes of data. Zero time of each histogram is 5 msec before the onset of the electric input to the earphone. Stimuli: tone time, approximately 10 bursts/sec. Each burst was turned on at the same phase.

Unit	Burst level	Unit	Burst level
36	−60 db	38	−50 db
34	−70 db	26	−60 db
33	−70 db	27	−70 db
43	−60 db	41	−70 db

UNIT 277-29
PST HISTOGRAMS

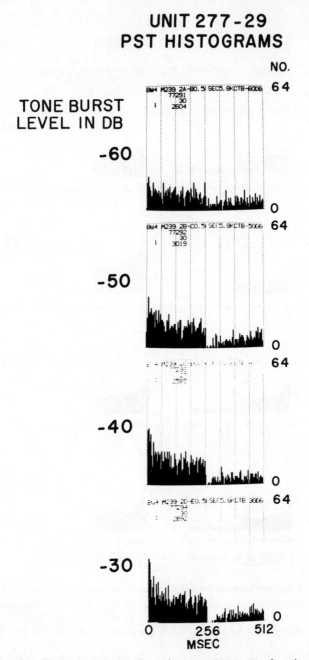

Figure 6.2 Response patterns of a unit to tone bursts as a function of stimulus level.

Zero time of each histogram is 2.5 msec before the onset of the electric input to the earphone. Stimuli: tone bursts, 5.8 kc (the CF of the unit), 250-msec duration, 2.5-msec rise-fall time.

Thus it is unlikely that the efferent system mentioned in Chapter 3 would play an important role in producing this pattern.

The peak at the onset of a burst is less prominent for low stimulus levels (Figure 6.2). At higher stimulus levels the transient peak becomes more prominent, as does the transient decrease in baseline activity following the termination of the burst. For primary units the time course of increased activity lasts as long as the duration of the stimulus. We never saw responses restricted to either the onset or termination of the tone bursts that could not be accounted for by the spectrum characteristics of the bursts (Sandel and Kiang, 1961); nor did we ever find after-discharges following the bursts.

6.2   Response Patterns to Noise Bursts

The time patterns of responses to bursts of noise are similar to the patterns for tone bursts. Figure 6.3 shows the familiar peak at the onset becoming more prominent at higher intensities, as does the decrease in baseline activity after the burst is turned off. The pattern of responses is typical for all units studied with stimulation by bursts of noise. The absence of specific "off" responses supports an earlier suggestion that the auditory nerve fibers do not discharge synchronously at the termination of noise bursts (Kiang and Sandel, 1961).

6.3   Effects of Changing Burst Parameters

The patterns of responses to tone and noise bursts change systematically as burst rate and burst duration are varied. Figure 6.4 shows that the peak at the onset becomes less prominent as bursts of constant duration are presented at higher rates. The interval histograms show two peaks — one peak corresponding to the short intervals between responses in each burst and the second peak at longer intervals corresponding to the interburst time. As the burst rate increases, the latter peak moves toward the former until they overlap. Similar changes are seen as burst duration is increased while burst rate is held constant (Figure 6.5). As burst duration increases, the two peaks in the interval histogram overlap and the peak at the onset becomes less prominent in the PST histograms.

The changes in time patterns of responses to tone and noise bursts as functions of intensity, burst rate, and burst duration might be at least qualitatively explainable in terms of the adaptive properties of the peripheral auditory system. The onsets of the burst become less

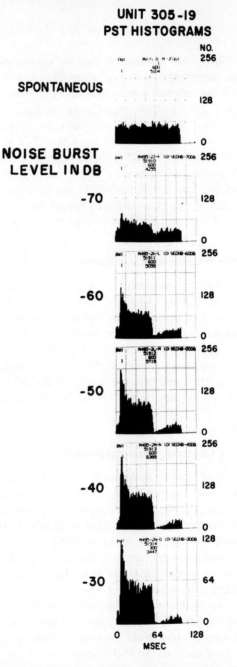

Figure 6.3 Response pattern of a unit to bursts of noise as a function of stimulus level.

CF: 4.49 kc. Stimuli: noise bursts, 50-msec duration, 2.5-msec rise-fall time, 10 bursts/sec. Reference level for noise bursts: 70.7 V rms into condenser earphone. Each histogram represents 1 minute of data except at −30 db when only 30 seconds of data were obtained. Zero time of each histogram is 2.5 msec before the onset of the electric input to the earphone.

effective in eliciting responses as the stimulus conditions approach low-level continuous stimulation; that is, when the burst level is low, the burst rate is high and the burst duration is long. Similar conclusions were reached in a study of the gross neural responses that were recorded near the round window (Peake, Kiang, and Goldstein, 1962).

6.4   Adaptation

In order to assess the effects of adaptation, we made measurements on discharge rates before, during, and after the presentation of single, long, tone bursts. From Figure 6.1, it appears that the level of activity reaches a plateau 30 msec after the burst onsets for 10/sec bursts of 50-msec duration at moderate stimulus levels. For single, long, tone bursts, however, changes in discharge rate may occur even after many minutes of stimulation. Figures 6.6 and 6.7 show the effects of stimulating with a very long tone burst on two units, one with low CF and the other with high CF. The scatter of points is considerable: there may even be slow regular fluctuations in rate. After 13 minutes of stimulation the activity has reached a steady level which is still significantly higher than the rate of spontaneous activity. We have not found adaptation to responses to levels at or below spontaneous rates. After the tone burst is turned off, there is a period of depressed activity with a slow return to the spontaneous level. The time course of the adaptation of unit discharges is comparable with the time course of loudness adaptation in normal human subjects (Hood, 1950; Egan, 1955).

It is sobering to recognize that long-term effects of stimulation may have had important effects on the quantitative measurements attempted in these studies. The order in which stimuli were presented and the insertion of silent periods may significantly alter rates of discharge. In general, the present data are derived from experiments in which the orders of stimulus presentations were from low to high stimulus levels, low to high rates, and from short to long duration. There were no significant intervening periods of silence between runs except where specifically noted. We hoped that by using such standard procedures the biasing effects would at least be systematic. We usually measured spontaneous activity at the start of each series of recordings and occasionally remeasured at later intervals. After contact with each unit was lost, many minutes usually elapsed; the standard click stimulation was maintained in searching for the next unit. Whenever possible, we avoided high-intensity stimulation except toward the end

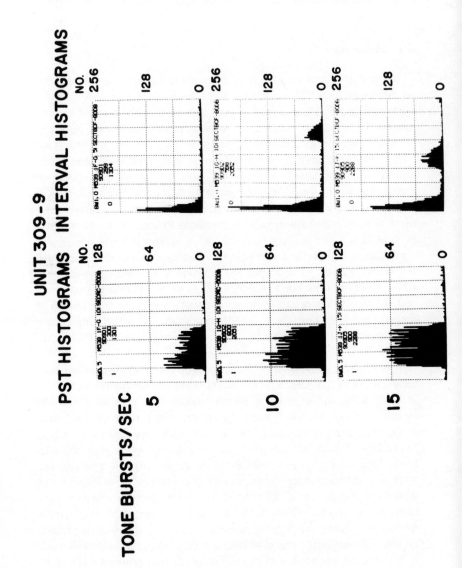

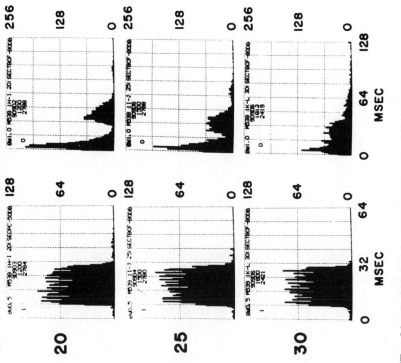

Figure 6.4 PST and interval histograms for a unit as rate of tone burst presentation is changed.

Zero time of each PST histogram is 2.5 msec before the onset of the electric input to the earphone. Stimuli: tone bursts, 1.45 kc (CF), 25-msec duration, 2.5-msec rise-fall time, −80 db.

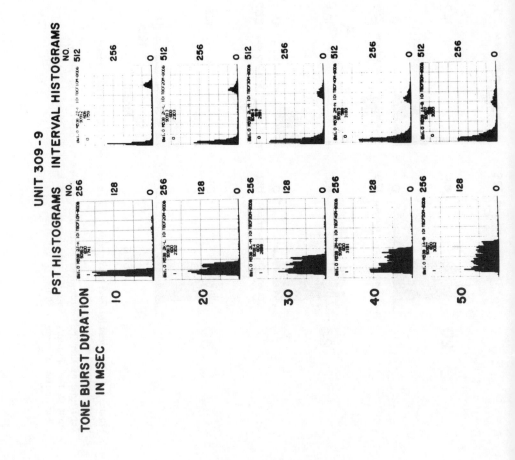

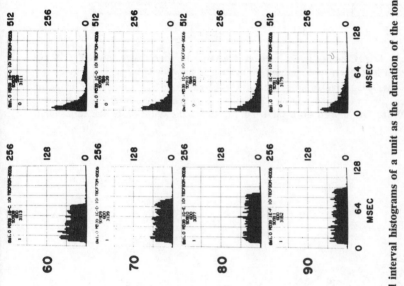

Figure 6.5 PST and interval histograms of a unit as the duration of the tone burst is changed.

Zero time of each PST histogram is 2.5 msec before the onset of the electric input to the earphone. Stimuli: tone bursts, 2.5-msec rise-fall time, approximately 10 bursts/sec, −80 db.

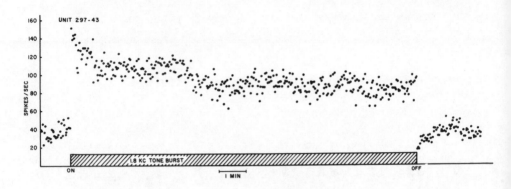

Figure 6.6   Changes in the rate of discharge of a unit with low CF (1.8 kc) when a tone burst of 13 minutes' duration is presented.

The data were divided into successive 1-second samples. Counts were made of every other 1-second sample. Stimulus: tone burst, 2.5-msec rise-fall time, −50 db. The shaded horizontal bar represents the duration of the tone burst.

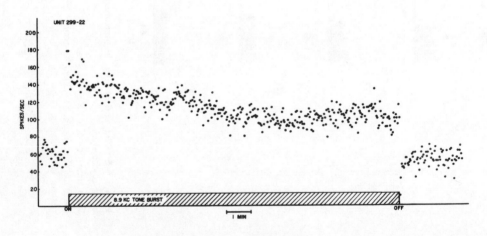

Figure 6.7   Changes in the rate of discharge of a unit with high CF (8.9 kc) when a tone burst of 13 minutes' duration is presented.

The data were divided into successive 1-second samples. Counts were made of every other 1-second sample. Stimulus: toneburst, 2.5-msec rise-fall time, −70 db. The shaded horizontal bar represents the duration of the tone burst.

of an experiment. In spite of our experimental precautions, we recommend a judicious attitude toward the quantitative results in this monograph wherever effects of adaptation may enter.

We can examine with greater time resolution the pattern of unit activity when continuous tones are presented. The unit in Figure 6.8 has a CF of 9.8 kc. Such a CF is too high for spikes to be time-locked to individual cycles of the stimulus; hence, the PST histograms are all flat and are not shown. The interval histograms for different stimulus levels are remarkably similar in shape, having a sharp rise followed by an exponential decay. As we shall see later in Figure 6.10, the discharge rate of this unit, taken for one-minute runs, rises to a maximum for tones at −80 db and falls with further increases in stimulus level. To check whether the decrease in discharge rate with increasing stimulus levels might be attributable to adaptation throughout the series of runs, each one-minute sample was divided into one-second samples. It was found that the rate of discharge was fairly constant throughout each one-minute sample. Thus adaptation may not be a sufficient explanation for the fall in intensity function at high stimulus levels.

6.5 Responses Time-Locked to Individual Cycles of Low-Frequency Tones

For units with low CF (below 4 to 5 kc), the discharges are time-locked to the individual cycles of a low-frequency tone (Figure 6.9). Note that there is only one peak in the PST histogram for each cycle. This is not always true for all units, particularly when the stimulus is presented at the higher levels. The interval histograms again show a fairly constant shape throughout the intensity series.

For units with high CF, there are discharges time-locked to individual cycles of a low-frequency tone only at high stimulus levels.

6.6 Intensity Functions for Tones at the CF

Figure 6.10 plots intensity functions for a number of units. Almost all of these units have a maximum rate of steady discharge that is reached within 20 to 50 db of threshold. For some units this maximum occurs at rather low stimulus levels. The range of stimulus level over which discharge rate changes is much smaller than either the range over which loudness judgments can be made psychophysically or the range over which microphonic potentials measured at the round window increase in amplitude (Stevens and Davis, 1938; Wever and

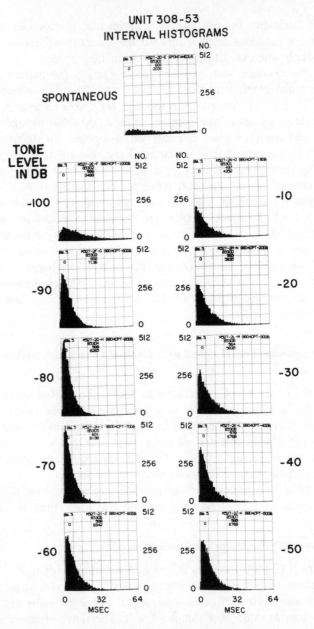

Figure 6.8 Interval histograms of discharges from a unit as the level of a continuous tone at 9.8 kc (CF) is changed in 10-db increments.

UNIT 326-3

PST HISTOGRAMS   INTERVAL HISTOGRAMS

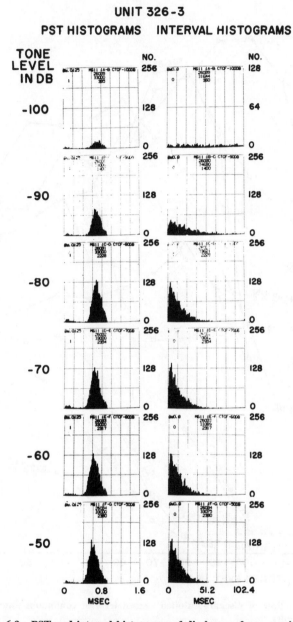

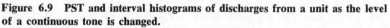

Figure 6.9   PST and interval histograms of discharges from a unit as the level of a continuous tone is changed.

The PST histograms were computed by triggering from stimulus markers at the positive zero crossing of the electric input to the earphone. Since the frequency of tone was 1.1 kc (CF), the PST histograms stop at 0.91 msec.

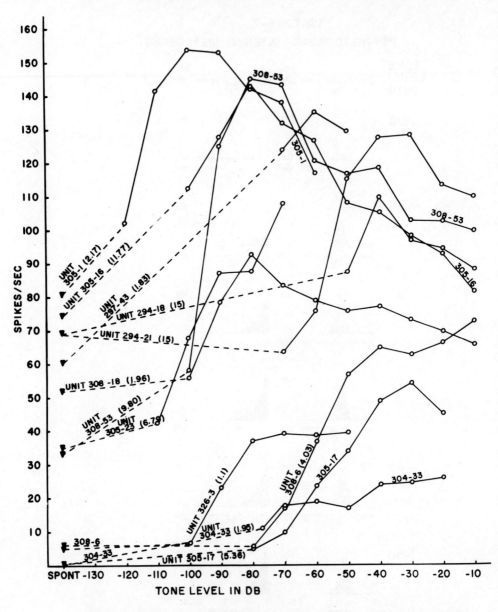

Figure 6.10 Rate of discharge plotted against level of continuous tone at the CF for 12 units.

The CF of the units are given in parentheses after the unit numbers. The dotted lines serve only to indicate the spontaneous rate of discharge (black triangles) that goes with each curve.

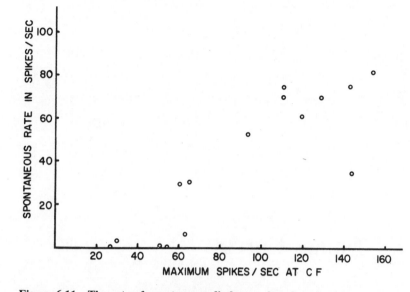

Figure 6.11 **The rate of spontaneous discharge plotted against the maximum rate of discharge elicited by tones at the CF.**

The maximum rate of discharge was determined from the peak of the intensity function for each unit.

Lawrence, 1954). Clearly, the rate of discharge in a single unit is not sufficient to specify the level of a stimulus. The comparison of these curves with the intensity functions for clicks (Figures 5.5 and 5.6) shows that the departure from monotonicity may also be a function of the duration of the stimulus.

Examination of Figure 6.10 seems to indicate a rough correlation between the spontaneous rate of activity and the maximum rate of discharge in response to continuous tones. This relationship is supported somewhat by Figure 6.11. Most units with high rates of spontaneous activity also have a high maximum rate of steady discharge under continuous stimulation.

Significantly, the maximum rate of steady discharge for any unit under continuous stimulation remains well below 200/sec although it is, of course, possible to reach higher rates for very short times, such as during the onset of an intense tone burst. We find that there is good agreement between these results and earlier results in studies on single units of other parts of the nervous system as summarized by Wever (1949).

7. Tuning Curves

7.1 The Determination of Tuning Curves

Although we have thus far emphasized time patterns of responses, most auditory physiologists have been especially concerned with response areas and tuning curves as obtained by the use of tonal stimuli. In this study response areas and tuning curves were determined for several hundred primary units. These determinations of response areas were always incomplete because measurements were not usually attempted for high stimulus levels that might have resulted in sustained injury to the cochlea. No "holes" were ever found in response areas because all tones with parameters within the tuning curves elicited spike responses.

In determining tuning curves, we found it necessary to define a "pragmatic threshold," that is, a stimulus condition for which the unit's behavior changes in a manner that is either visually or auditorily clearly detectable. When a trained investigator repeatedly determines tuning curves for the same unit, there is great consistency in the sense that for any given frequency the pragmatic threshold falls within 5 to 10 db. Using PST histograms, the levels at which a response is detectable are consistently lower. The difference ranges from 5 to 20 db depending upon the unit's CF and rate of spontaneous discharges. In most of the "threshold" determinations in this monograph, we also used a counter to monitor the rate of spike discharges. Our visual criteria corresponded, roughly, to a 10 to 20 per cent increase in discharge rate over the rate of spontaneous discharge for tone-burst

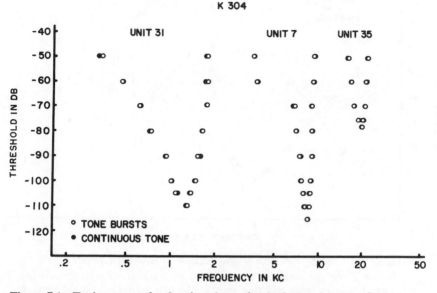

Figure 7.1 Tuning curves for 3 units taken using both tone bursts and continuous tones.

The frequency scale is logarithmic. Stimuli: tone bursts, 50-msec duration, 2.5-msec rise-fall time, 10 bursts/sec. Units 31 and 35 were run with tone bursts first, then continuous tone. For Unit 7, the reverse procedure was followed.

stimulation, as defined in the caption for Figure 7.1. Since threshold determinations are affected by adaptation phenomena, we tried to avoid high stimulus levels in order to minimize whatever adaptation phenomena were present.

Figure 7.1 shows that tuning curves obtained using tone bursts are the same as those obtained using continuous tones. If the onset times of the bursts become very short, there is, of course, spread of energy to other frequencies (Sandel and Kiang, 1961). This spectral broadening would result in broader tuning curves.*

It has been suggested that the manner of obtaining threshold points can influence the shape of tuning curves (Tasaki, 1960), but Figure 7.2 shows that this is not a significant factor in our study. Figures 7.3, 7.4, and 7.5 show sample tuning curves from a number of animals. The use of a logarithmic scale for frequency tends to make the curves look sharper at the high frequencies. There has been much

---

* It is also important to keep the electronic switching artifacts of the bursts at levels that are low relative to the threshold of the unit.

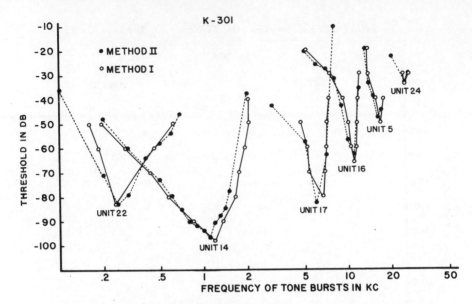

Figure 7.2 Tuning curves of 6 units taken by 2 different methods.

Method I was the standard method used throughout the rest of the study in which a level is set and frequency of the tone bursts is changed until the unit responds or fails to respond. The limits of the range of frequencies to which the unit is responsive are indicated by open dots at each level. In Method II, the frequency is set and the level is increased until a response is obtained.

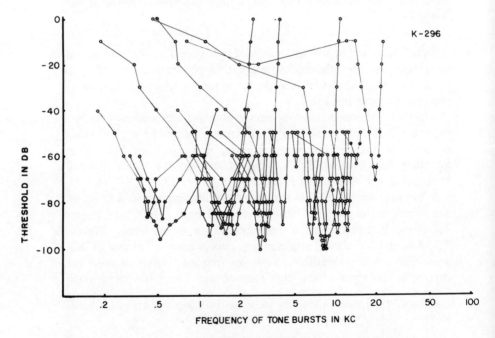

Figure 7.3 Sample tuning curves taken by Method I from a single cat.

The points near the tip of the tuning curves were taken with special care. Only the last few units could be run at high stimulus levels since intense stimuli tended to have long-lasting effects on the thresholds of subsequently obtained units.

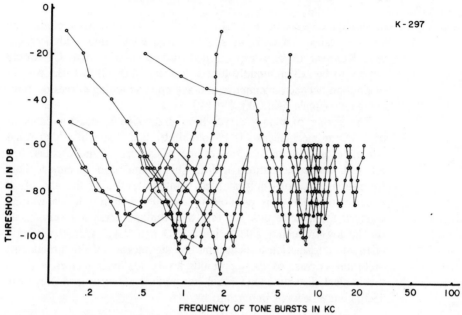

Figure 7.4   Sample tuning curves taken by Method I from a single cat.
See Figure 7.3

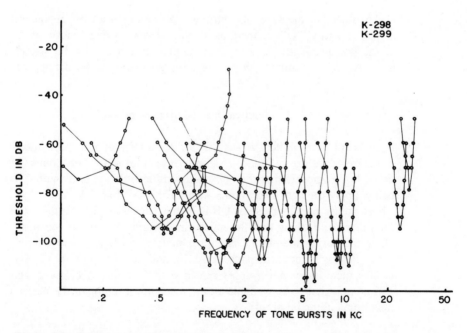

Figure 7.5   Tuning curves from 2 cats combined to show a wider range of CF than was shown in Figures 7.3 and 7.4.

discussion concerning the "sharpness" of tuning curves plotted on various scales. On a linear scale of frequency, units with low CF would appear to be sharply tuned and units with high CF would appear to be rather broadly tuned. It seems difficult to make a clear distinction between symmetric and asymmetric tuning curves on plots using either scale (Katsuki, 1961).

The shapes of tuning curves have great significance for concepts of cochlear mechanisms. It is sometimes said that while high tones stimulate only limited regions of the basal turn of the cochlea, low tones stimulate the entire cochlea. This formulation appears to hold for primary neurons only at high stimulus levels. At the end of an experiment when it is possible to use high stimulus levels without concern for later results, we find that tuning curves are very broad on the low-frequency side (Figures 7.3 and 7.4). We do not have adequate information to determine the significance of this broadening of tuning curves. At these stimulus levels nonlinear factors, such as mechanical distortion and aural harmonics, (Stevens and Newman, 1936) may become important.

7.2   Sharpness of Tuning Curves

An objective measure of sharpness of tuning used by engineers is the quantity *"Q"* defined as center frequency/bandwidth at 3 db above threshold. A somewhat similar measure may be useful here. A *"Q"* for tuning curves may, for convenience, be defined as

$$"Q" = \frac{CF}{\text{bandwidth at 10 db re threshold}}$$

If such *"Q"* are plotted versus CF for a number of units, an interesting relationship is found (Figure 7.6): the scatter of points is great, but it appears that the *"Q"* values differ little for units with CF below approximately 2 kc. Units with CF higher than 2 kc have *"Q"* whose values may increase as CF is higher. Békésy's observations, on the other hand, show that the mechanical tuning at various locations along the basilar membrane is approximately constant (1960); however, Békésy's measurements were limited to the portion of the basilar membrane that is most sensitive to frequencies below 2 kc, and no information is available on the mechanical tuning of the basilar membrane in the basal turn.

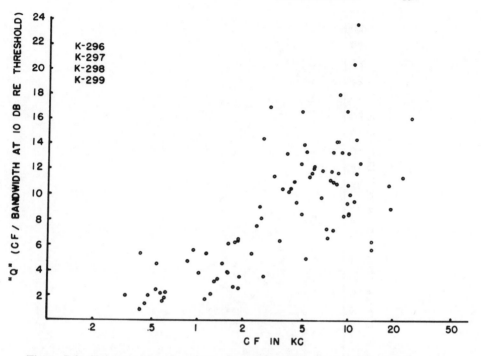

Figure 7.6 Sharpness of tuning, "*Q*", of primary units as a function of CF.
Each point represents one unit, and the total graph represents data from 4
different cats in which the experimental conditions were kept as comparable
as possible. Tuning curves were obtained as in Figure 7.3. Here "*Q*" is defined
as CF/bandwidth of the tuning curve at a level of 10 db above the threshold
at CF. Usually Q is defined as center frequency/bandwidth at 3 db re
threshold, but this definition is not practical for the present measurements.

7.3 "Thresholds"

The lowest point on a tuning curve shows the unit's threshold at
the CF. Thresholds for different units vary greatly (Appendix A),
and the variation seems to bear no obvious relationship to the sharpness of the tuning curves (Figure 7.7). However, it may not be proper
to compare threshold values for units at different CF's since the
maximum sensitivity of units varies considerably with CF.

Figure 7.8 shows threshold values at CF for many units. The general shape of the curve formed by points representing the most
sensitive units resembles markedly the audiograms obtained by behavioral techniques (Neff and Hind, 1955; Elliot, Stein, and Harrison,
1960; Miller, Watson, and Covell, 1963). Undoubtedly, the increase

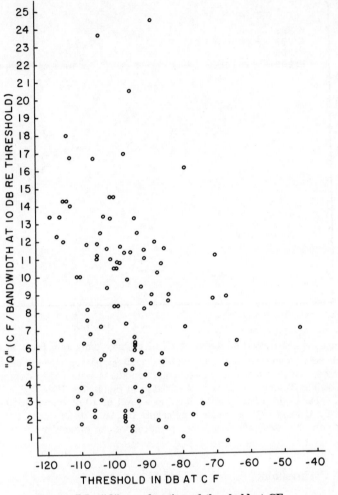

Figure 7.7 "*Q*" **as a function of threshold at CF.**

in thresholds at high frequencies is at least partially attributable to the response characteristics of the middle ear and the output character-istics of the earphone. The increase of thresholds at low frequencies and the lack of units with low thresholds having CF between 2 and 5 kc are more difficult to explain. The behavioral audiogram also shows an increase in threshold at low frequencies and a rise around 4 kc. Since the points in Figure 7.8 represent single units, the explana-tions of these particular features in the audiogram need not be based

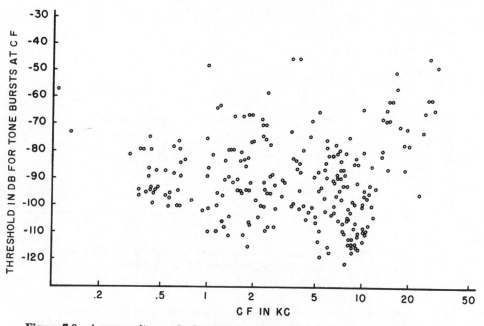

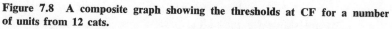

Figure 7.8   A composite graph showing the thresholds at CF for a number of units from 12 cats.

It is possible to convert the levels to sound-pressure levels at the eardrum by using Figure 2.3.

on density of innervation (Schuknecht, 1960; Finck and Berlin, 1965). Both the earphone and the middle ear are essentially "flat" (below 2 kc). The "notch" between 2 and 5 kc may be, in part, due to the acoustic characteristics of the middle-ear and bulla cavities (Møller). In a number of experiments in this laboratory a similar, although sharper, notch (which is seen in plots of amplitude versus frequency for cochlear microphonics) disappears if the small hole connecting the middle-ear and bulla cavities is sealed with bone wax. A complete explanation of the shape of the behavioral audiogram in terms of physiological mechanisms is still lacking (Wever, 1949).

We have pooled data from many animals to obtain Figure 7.8 (Appendix A). These animals were selected so that their thresholds for click responses recorded at the round window were within 5 db of one another. The wide variation in thresholds for units with the same CF is not explained by the pooling of data from different cats since results from individual animals show almost as great a spread of points. Variations in the resonant frequencies of the acoustic sys-

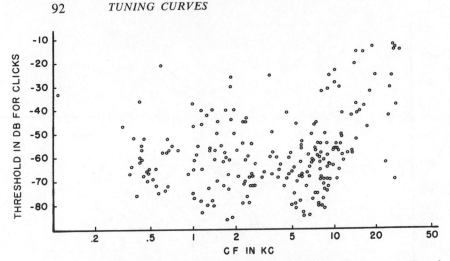

Figure 7.9 The thresholds to clicks plotted against the CF for a number of units from the 12 cats from which Figure 7.8 was derived.
Reference level was 100 V into condenser earphones.

tem from cat to cat may contribute to the spread of points at frequencies above 10 kc but are negligible at lower frequencies. Thresholds are stable for individual units unless high stimulus levels are used, in which case the threshold may be increased by as much as 20 db for many minutes. Apparently, units that have the same CF may have grossly different thresholds.

When thresholds for response to clicks are plotted against CF (Figure 7.9), the distribution of points (at least for points below 10 kc) is very similar to that in Figure 7.8. The differences between Figures 7.8 and 7.9 are explainable in terms of the click spectrum; there is less energy at the higher frequencies. The similarities of the two plots suggest that primary units behave as if they are preceded by narrow band filters so that each unit is influenced by a particular range of frequency components.

Although the tuning curves have been defined in terms of an increase in discharge rate above the spontaneous level, decreases in discharge rate must also be considered responses. However, in no instance has a tone burst alone resulted in a decrease in discharge rate either at the onset of a burst or throughout duration of a burst. In this sense tone bursts have not been shown to decrease baseline activity.

8. Spontaneous Activity

8.1 Definition of Spontaneous Activity

As indicated in the foregoing chapters, auditory nerve fibers exhibit spontaneous discharges as well as responses to sound. We cannot define spontaneous activity as activity in the absence of sound since it is virtually impossible to eliminate completely all extraneous acoustic stimuli. The normal threshold of hearing is so low that even Brownian motion of the air may be detectable. For this reason we define spontaneous activity as activity in the absence of sound controlled by the experimenter.

In addition to the Brownian motion of the air molecules, there is the "noise" produced by molecular motion in the biological structures of the middle and inner ear (Sivian and White, 1933; de Vries, 1952). In the present study ambient airborne noise was minimized by conducting all experiments in a soundproof chamber with a closed acoustic system from tympanic earphone to membrane. Unfortunately, it is not feasible to eliminate sounds that are generated by the animal, such as those produced by breathing or heartbeats.*

* After the cochlea is destroyed in acute experiments by a blunt probe, spontaneous discharges are not found although brief bursts of spikes may appear as the micropipette is moved within the nerve.

8.2   Rates of Spontaneous Activity

All units examined displayed some spontaneous activity. The rate of spontaneous discharge for a particular unit was stable unless high stimulus levels had been used previously. The rates for different units varied from less than 6 spikes/min to approximately 100 spikes/sec. Figure 8.1 shows spontaneous discharges from three units in the same cat; the CF for the three units differ little, suggesting that something more than ambient acoustic noise is necessary to account for the differences in rates of spontaneous discharges for different units.

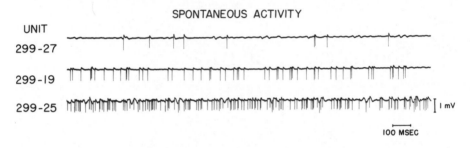

Figure 8.1   Spike trains of activity in 3 units from the same animal.
The 3 units were selected because their tuning curves were nearly identical. The CF for the units were 10.06 kc, 11.6 kc, and 10.95 kc respectively; the rates of spontaneous discharges for the 3 units were 4.3, 38.3, and 72.0 spikes/sec, respectively. Less than an hour elapsed between the recording from Unit 299-25 and that from Unit 299-27.

Figure 8.2 demonstrates that the rate of spontaneous discharges is indeed independent of CF, while Figure 8.3 suggests that it is possible to obtain adjacent units with very different rates of spontaneous discharges in a single electrode track. Furthermore, our data show no systematic trends in rates with time and indicate that no long-term physiological variables, such as surgical shock or depth of anesthesia, can account for the different rates of spontaneous discharges.

8.3   Time Patterns of Spontaneous Activity

Examination of the spike trains in Figure 8.1 shows that the discharges appear to be irregular in time pattern. Quantitative methods for studying the time patterns have been described previously in studies

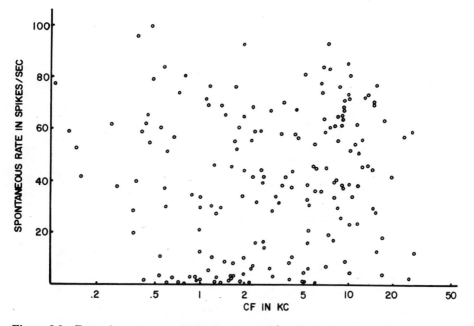

Figure 8.2   Rate of spontaneous discharges from 185 units in 29 cats plotted against their CF.

of single units in the cochlear nucleus (Rodieck, Kiang, and Gerstein, 1962). These methods dealt primarily with interspike-interval histograms and made it possible to show that at least four different time patterns of spontaneous activity can be found in the cochlear nucleus. The interspike-interval histograms of the spontaneous activity of the three units in Figure 8.1 are shown in Figure 8.4. For comparison, the histograms have been plotted on the same scale even though the responses for Unit 299-27 are too few in number to reveal the details of the shape of its histogram for this scale. The shapes of such histograms for primary units all have certain common features: the histograms rise quickly to a peak, usually before 10 msec, followed by a decay that appears to be exponential. Longer samples of data for three different units, with high, medium, and low rate of spontaneous discharge, have been plotted on semilogarithmic scales in Figures 8.5, 8.6, and 8.7, respectively. Except when the scatter of points is too great because of insufficient numbers of responses, the decays from the modal values are reasonably well fitted by straight lines and may, to a first approximation, be considered exponential. The joint-interval

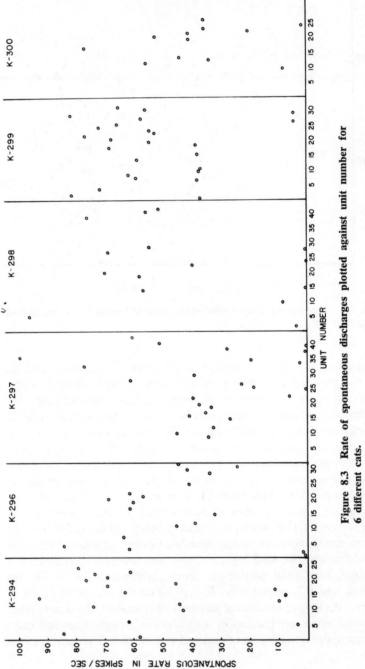

Figure 8.3 Rate of spontaneous discharges plotted against unit number for 6 different cats.

The unit number gives an indication of the time sequence in which units were obtained.

SPONTANEOUS ACTIVITY

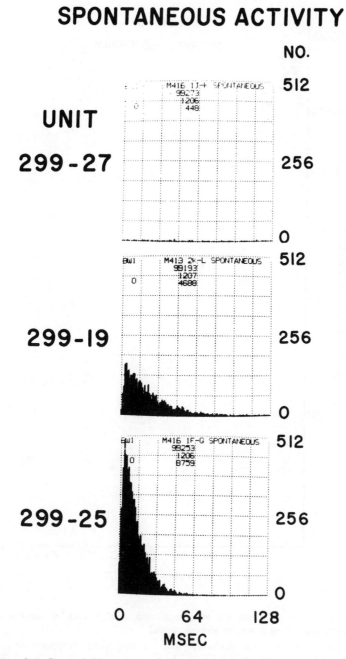

Figure 8.4 Interval histograms of the spontaneous activity for the 3 units shown in Figure 8.1.

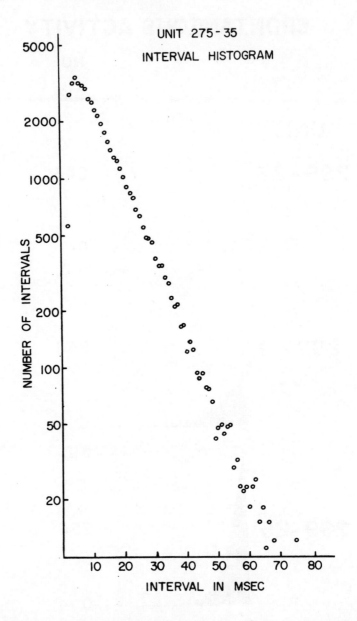

Figure 8.5 Interval histogram of a unit with a high rate of spontaneous discharges plotted on a semilogarithmic scale.

The rate of spontaneous discharges was 76 spikes/sec. Approximately 11 minutes of data are represented. CF: 7.3 kc.

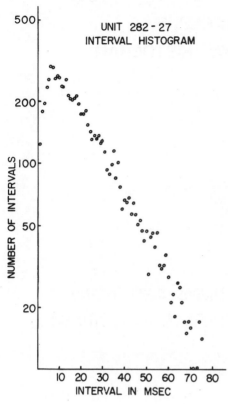

UNIT 282-27
INTERVAL HISTOGRAM

Figure 8.6 Interval histogram of a unit with a medium rate of spontaneous discharges plotted on a semilogarithmic scale.

The rate of spontaneous discharges was 45.5 spikes/sec. Three minutes of data are represented. CF: 0.58 kc.

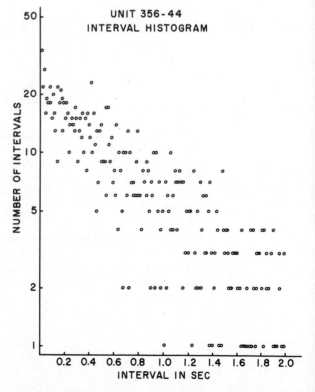

UNIT 356-44
INTERVAL HISTOGRAM

Figure 8.7 Interval histogram of a unit with low rate of spontaneous discharges plotted on a semilogarithmic scale.

The rate of spontaneous discharges was 1.9 spikes/sec. 7.9 minutes of data are represented. CF: 26 kc.

UNIT 275-35

SPONTANEOUS
JOINT INTERVAL HISTOGRAM

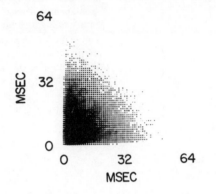

MEANS OF COLUMNS AND ROWS
IN THE JOINT INTERVAL HISTOGRAM

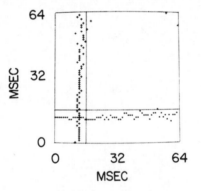

Figure 8.8   Upper plot: a joint-interval histogram for the spontaneous activity of an auditory nerve fiber.

The interval histogram for the spontaneous activity of this unit is shown in Figure 8.5. The abscissa represents the duration of τ_1, the first of each pair of successive intervals, the ordinate represents duration of τ_2, the second of each pair of intervals. The number of interval pairs which occur with (τ_1, τ_2) values is represented by the intensity of the spot at coordinates (τ_1, τ_2).

Lower plot: the means of each row and column of the joint-interval histogram immediately above.

Row means (crosses) are plotted against columns; column means (dots) are plotted against rows. The vertical and horizontal straight lines are present only for purposes of comparison.

histogram for Unit 275-35 shown in Figure 8.8 is typical for primary units.* The joint-interval histogram and the means of columns and rows in the joint-interval histogram can give some indication of the degree to which successive intervals are independent.

In comparing the statistical properties of spontaneous activity with those of a Poisson process, we find some similarities and one important difference. In a Poisson process successive intervals are independent. Figure 8.8 suggests that it may be reasonable to regard the intervals between spikes as being independent. The interval distribution of a Poisson process is a decaying exponential function where the time constant of the decay is determined by the rate of the process. The interval histogram of spontaneous activity has a roughly exponential decay from its mode. However, if the spontaneous activity were generated by a Poisson process, one would expect a greater number of short intervals than are found in the histograms. This difference represents a brief reduction in the probability of firing following each discharge. This reduction is not present in a Poisson process and is presumably a consequence of the refractory properties of the units.

Figure 8.9 shows that the modes for the interval histograms nearly all fall within 4 and 7 msec regardless of the rate of discharges. This fact suggests that beyond a certain time after each discharge we may consider the unit to be "recovered."

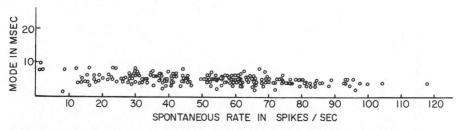

Figure 8.9 The mode of the interval histograms of spontaneous activity plotted against rate of spontaneous discharges for 227 auditory nerve fibers. Each histogram is based on at least 1 minute of data. For units with low rates of spontaneous discharges only long runs of data are meaningful.

8.4 Distribution of Rates of Spontaneous Activity among Units

Do the rates of spontaneous discharge form a normal distribution? Figure 8.10 shows that they do not; rather, they seem to be grouped around certain preferred rates. Despite the ever-present possibility of biased sampling of units, there is clearly a large group of units with

* The details of the computation have been discussed by Rodieck, Kiang, and Gerstein, 1962.

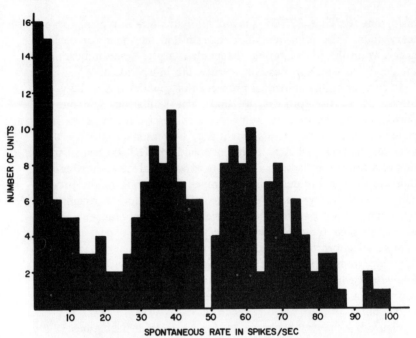

Figure 8.10 Histogram of rates of spontaneous discharges.
206 units from 29 cats are represented. The bin width is 2.5 spikes/sec.

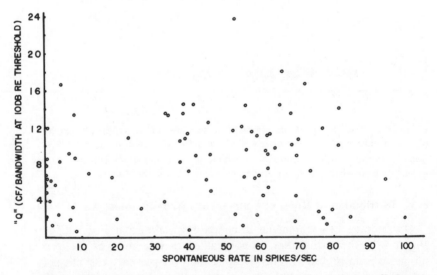

Figure 8.11 "Q" for 84 units plotted against rate of spontaneous discharges.
(See Figure 7.6.)

less than 5 spikes/sec. A similar group of units with low rates of spontaneous discharges has been found in the monkey (Nomoto, Suga, and Katsuki, 1964). The dips at 50 and 65 spikes/sec suggest that there may be other groupings. The appearance of discrete peaks cannot be explained by the pooling of data from many animals where all units from one animal show low rates of spontaneous discharges and all units from another show high rates. The discrete groupings are discernible even in individual animals (Figure 8.3). What can be the significance of the groupings in Figure 8.10? They cannot be related to the longitudinal location along the cochlear partition that is innervated by the fibers (Figure 8.2). They do not appear to be related to the longitudinal extent of the innervated region (Figure 8.11).

One of the recurring speculations concerning cochlear functions has been that the inner hair cells may be less sensitive than the outer hair cells (Stevens and Davis, 1938). Almost any characteristic of units which cannot be related to locus of innervation longitudinally along the cochlear partition is a candidate for differentiating units innervating inner and outer hair cells. Apparently there are large differences in threshold among primary units; units having the same CF may have thresholds that differ by as much as 60 db. Figure 8.12

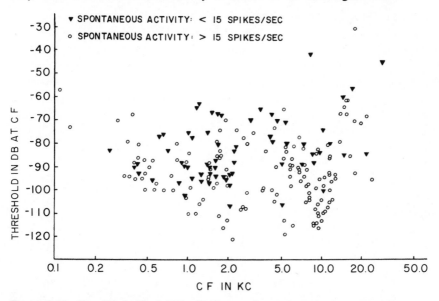

Figure 8.12   The threshold of 205 units from a large number of cats plotted against CF.

The units that have low rates of spontaneous discharges are shown with solid triangles; units with higher rates of spontaneous discharges are shown with open circles. The data for this plot are found in Table 10.1.

shows that there is some tendency for units with low rates of spontaneous activity to have higher thresholds than other units with comparable CF. (The data for this figure may be found in Appendix A.) Perhaps better measurements and more explicit criteria of thresholds will demonstrate a clearer connection between spontaneous activity and thresholds. It may even be that the groupings of Figure 8.10 relate to the one row of inner hair cells and the three rows of outer hair cells in the cochlea; but the present data are too tenuous to support so specific a hypothesis.

9. Responses to Combinations of "Simple" Acoustic Stimuli

The preceding chapters demonstrate that responses of primary units to "simple" stimuli are to some extent predictable if certain measures of response characteristics, such as CF, threshold at CF, and rate of spontaneous activity, are known. It is important to determine whether responses to combinations of simple stimuli are predictable by combining the response patterns to the individual stimuli.

9.1 Responses to Click and Tone Bursts in the Presence of Background Noise

One of the most familiar psychophysical phenomena that involve combinations of stimuli is masking. Masking has been defined as " . . . the number of decibels by which a listener's threshold of audibility for a given tone is raised by the presence of another sound" (Stevens and Davis, 1938). It has long been known that the addition of broad-band noise will reduce or abolish the amplitude of the neural potentials recorded at the round window (Stevens and Davis, 1938; Rosenblith, 1950; Davis, 1957). This reduction of neural potentials is presumably a physiological correlate of the masking phenomenon and has been attributed to a "line-busy" effect (Davis and Derbyshire, 1935; Stevens and Davis, 1938; Goldstein and Kiang, 1958). According to this conception the noise activates some of the nerve fibers so that

105

UNIT 309-17

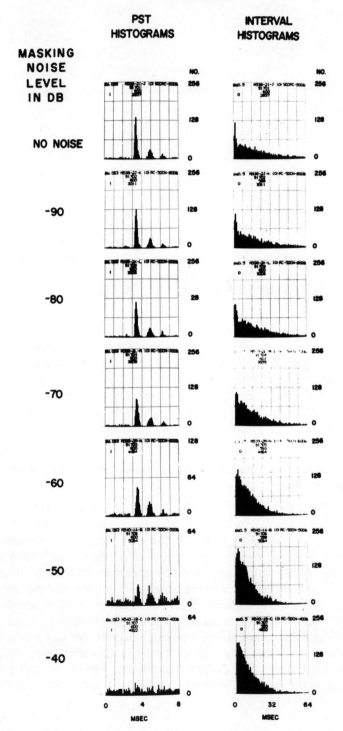

PST HISTOGRAMS   INTERVAL HISTOGRAMS

MASKING NOISE LEVEL IN DB

NO NOISE

-90

-80

-70

-60

-50

-40

MSEC

the click encounters many fibers that are in a refractory state and unable to respond.

The effect of a continuous broadband noise on the click response of an auditory nerve fiber is shown in Figure 9.1. The interval histogram of the activity under the "no-noise" condition shows a peak at 1.5 msec. This peak corresponds to the characteristic period of the unit (1/CF of the unit = 1.4 msec). As the level of the noise is increased, the interval histogram approaches that of spontaneous activity of a unit with a high rate of spontaneous discharge. At −40 db of noise the peak at 1.5 msec is not distinguishable as a separate peak. The rate of discharges increases from 47.6 spikes/sec under the no-noise condition to 82.0 spikes/sec under the −40-db noise condition.

The PST histograms in Figure 9.1 show more clearly the effect of the noise on the multiple peaks of the click response pattern. The latencies of the peaks do not change as the level of the noise is increased, and there is an absence of activity between the peaks even though the baseline activity is raised considerably. As noise level is increased, the baseline activity does not rise to overshadow the click response in the PST histogram; instead, the peaks representing the responses are clearly reduced as the baseline activity increases. The effect of increasing the level of noise may be compared to the effect of decreasing click level (Chapter 5).

Figure 9.2 shows that, as the noise level is increased, the height of the first peak in the PST histogram falls more rapidly than that of the second peak. At −50 db, the first two peaks are nearly equal in height. At the −40-db level of noise the two peaks become more difficult to distinguish from baseline activity.

The effect of continuous broadband noise on responses to tone bursts is shown in Figure 9.3 for a unit with low CF and in Figure 9.4 for a unit with a higher CF. The onset peak of the tone response in the PST histogram seems to be most sensitive to the masking noise; thus, at the higher levels of noise, the response patterns to tone bursts appear almost as a plateau in the PST histogram. In Chapter 7, it was shown that under certain stimulus conditions the onset peak in

---

Figure 9.1   Masking responses to clicks by broadband noise.

Responses to clicks are shown as a function of noise level. PST and interval histograms of the same samples of data are shown. The threshold of the unit to clicks was −68 db by visual determination. CF: 0.7 kc. The initial peak in the interval histograms corresponds to the intervals between multiple responses. Note especially the changes in vertical scale. Stimuli: 10/sec clicks, −50 db re 100 V into condenser earphone; noise reference level: 70.7 V rms into condenser earphone.

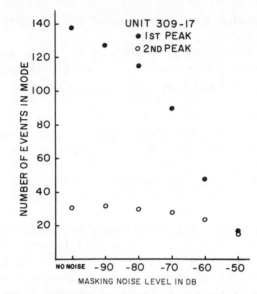

Figure 9.2 The modal value of the first 2 peaks in the PST histogram of Figure 9.2 plotted against the level of background noise.

the PST histogram could be selectively depressed. The presence of masking noise appears to be yet another of these conditions.

In Figure 9.3, the rate of discharge was 63.2 spikes/sec under the no-noise condition and 58.6 spikes/sec when the highest level of noise was present. In Figure 9.4, the rate of discharge was 111.7 spikes/sec under the no-noise condition and 79.3 spikes/sec when the highest level of noise was present. Thus the rate of discharges when tone bursts and noise are presented together seems to be lower than that when tone bursts are presented alone. This phenomenon is seen for units with both high and low CF, for units with both high and low rates of spontaneous activity, and for units with both high and low thresholds.

With a simple line-busy explanation one might have expected the over-all rate of discharge to increase after adding noise to the tone bursts. Since rather opposite results are obtained, other explanations should be considered. In Chapter 5, it was suggested that movement of the cochlear partition in one direction resulted in increased activity but movement in the opposite direction resulted in decreased activity in auditory nerve fibers. It may be that a similar mechanism is at work to reduce the response to tone bursts when noise is presented. The effects of adaptation should also be considered.

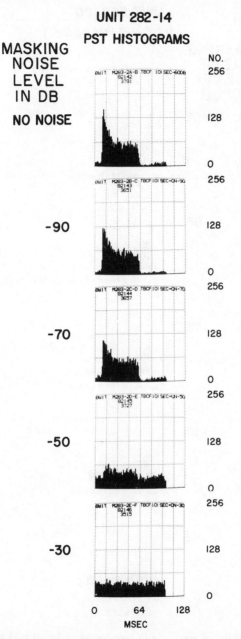

Figure 9.3 Masking of responses to tone bursts by broadband noise. Each histogram represents 1 minute of data.

The total number of spikes processed for each histogram was 3791 for no noise, 3651 for −90 db, 3657 for −70 db, 3727 for −50 db, and 3515 for −30 db. Zero time of each histogram is 5 msec before the onset of the electric input to the earphone. Stimuli: tone bursts, 2.0 kc (CF), 50-msec duration, 5-msec rise-fall time; 10 bursts/sec, −60 db re 5 V P-P into dynamic earphone.

UNIT 282-20
PST HISTOGRAMS

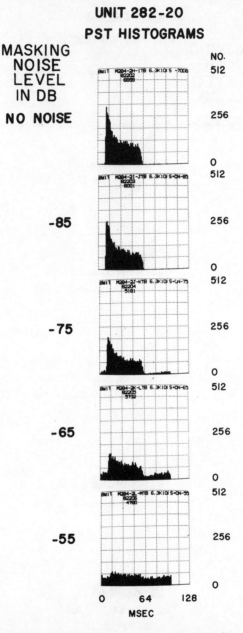

Figure 9.4 **Masking of responses to tone bursts by broadband noise.**

Each histogram represents 1 minute of data. The total number of spikes processed for each histogram was 6691 for no noise, 6001 for −85 db, 5181 for −75 db, 5732 for −65 db, and 4760 for −55 db. Zero time of each histogram is 5 msec before the onset of the electric input to the earphone. Stimuli: tone bursts, 6.3 kc (CF), 50-msec duration, 5-msec rise-fall time, 10 bursts/sec, −70 db re 5 V P-P into dynamic earphone.

The presence of background noise also affects the tuning curves obtained by using tone bursts (Figure 9.5). The introduction of masking noise raises the detectable threshold at every frequency but does not appear to shift the CF. At the stimulus levels used in Figure 9.5, an increase in the level of noise by 20 db increased the threshold at CF by approximately 12 db; the increase in threshold at other frequencies is less. The question of whether these particular numbers are significant will probably have to await more reliable measures of threshold.

9.2   Responses to Two Tones That Beat

Another psychophysical phenomenon involving mixtures of simple acoustic stimuli is the perception of beats. When two tones close in frequency are presented together, they beat at a rate that is equal to the difference in the frequencies. The beating is a result of regular

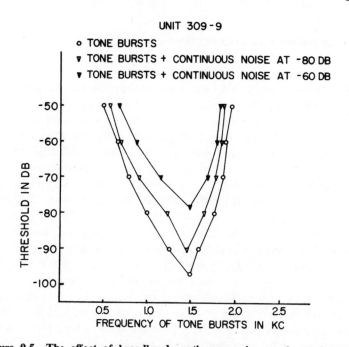

Figure 9.5   The effect of broadband continuous noise on the tuning curve. Tuning curves were taken under normal conditions and also in the presence of broadband noise at 2 different levels. The frequency scale is linear. Similar results are obtained for units with high CF.

addition and cancellation of the two tones. The unit in Figure 9.6 responds to both 1.532-kc and 1.527-kc tones presented singly by exhibiting irregular discharges. When both tones are presented together, Figure 9.6 shows that the unit responds by discharging in bursts that are synchronous with the beat frequency.

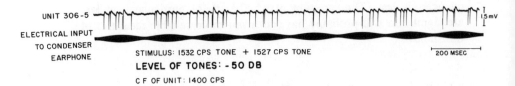

UNIT 306-5

ELECTRICAL INPUT
TO CONDENSER
EARPHONE

STIMULUS: 1532 CPS TONE + 1527 CPS TONE

LEVEL OF TONES: -50 DB

C F OF UNIT: 1400 CPS

200 MSEC

1.5 mV

Figure 9.6   Spike trains of a unit in response to a mixture of 2 tones that beat at 5 cycles/sec.
The unit responds to each tone by discharging irregularly but in bursts occurring at 5/sec (the beat frequency). The rate of spontaneous discharges was 14.6 spikes/sec. CF: 1.4 kc; level of tones: −50 db.

9.3   Responses with Complex Two-Stimulus Effects

The foregoing results of experiments, using masking noise and combinations of tones that beat, support the view that response patterns to combinations of stimuli are not obtained by simply summing responses to the component stimuli. Even more striking support is found in the following experiments involving the use of two stimuli.

Figure 9.7 shows a unit with high CF, clearly identifiable as an auditory nerve fiber by the short latency of its responses to clicks. This unit displays considerable spontaneous activity (100 spikes/sec), and a continuous tone at the CF increases the unit's rate of discharge. The unit responds to a tone burst that is 2.5 kc higher than its CF; this response has a time pattern that resembles those described in Chapter 7 for tone bursts at the CF. Thus the frequency and intensity of the tone bursts fall clearly within the tuning curve of this unit. The addition of the tone bursts to a background of a continuous tone at the CF results in a reduction of the unit's discharge rate to a level that is even below its rate of spontaneous discharge, and the latency of the reduction is precisely that of the response to tone bursts alone. There is an initial transient dip in the histogram, followed by a gradual increase to a plateau that is still lower than the level of spontaneous discharges. The envelope of the reduction is very nearly the inverse of the response pattern to the tone burst alone. When the

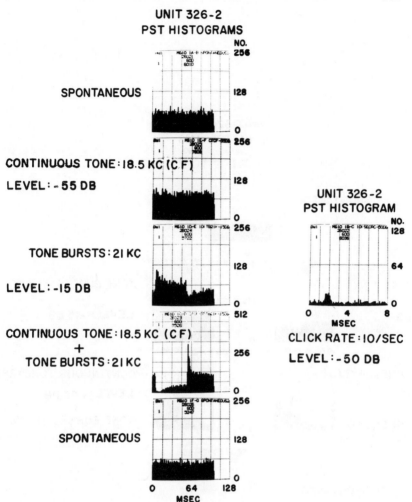

Figure 9.7 Response patterns of a unit with high CF to a combination of tone burst and background continuous tone.

The top histogram shows the level of spontaneous activity (100 spikes/sec). The second histogram shows that activity is increased in the presence of a continuous tone at the CF of the unit. The third histogram shows the response pattern of the unit to 21-kc tone bursts. The fourth histogram shows the results of combining the continuous tone and tone-burst stimuli. The bottom histogram is a control run of spontaneous activity. The zero time of these histograms is 2.5 msec before the onset of the electric input to the earphone. Stimuli: tone bursts, 50-msec duration, 2.5-msec rise-fall time, 10 bursts/sec, —15 db. Continuous tone level: —55 db. Since the tone-burst rate was 10/sec, the histograms on the left end at 100 msec. The single histogram on the right shows the latency of the click response. Stimuli: clicks, 10/sec, —50 db.

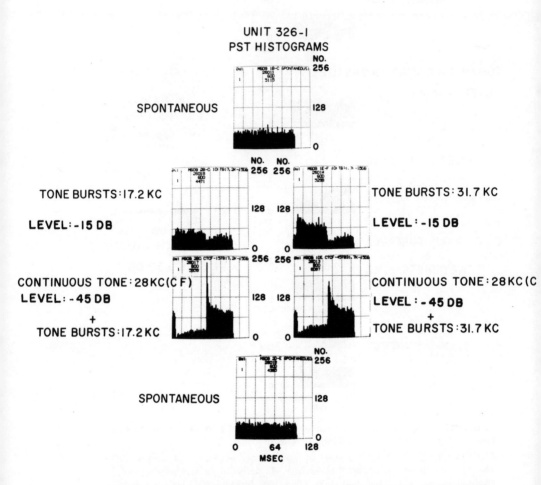

Figure 9.8 Response patterns of a unit with high CF to tone bursts at a frequency just within the tuning curve and to these same tone bursts in combination with a continuous tone at the CF.

Rate of spontaneous discharges: 85.4 spikes/sec. Zero time of the histograms is 2.5 msec before the onset of the electric input to the earphone. Stimuli: tone bursts, 50-msec duration, 2.5-msec rise-fall time, 10 bursts/sec, −15 db; continuous-tone level: −45 db.

tone burst is turned off, there is a large transient increase in discharge rate and a relatively quick return to the baseline level.

The reduction of activity occurs for tone bursts of frequencies both above and below the CF (Figures 9.8 and 9.9). It occurs not only for units with high CF but also for units with low CF (Figure 9.10). The reduction also occurs if the continuous tone is replaced by continuous broadband noise. In performing these experiments and in obtaining tuning curves, no instance was observed in which the level of spontaneous discharges could be reduced by presenting tone bursts alone.

The detailed elucidation of the mechanism by which addition of a tone burst reduces the level of discharges in the presence of a continuous tone must await a systematic examination of variables that affect this phenomenon. It seems unlikely that the efferent system is involved in this phenomenon, and there are a number of reasons for this conclusion. The short latency of the reduction argues against any central influence. The presence of a transient increase in activity after the reduction suggests that the crossed olivo-cochlear bundle does not

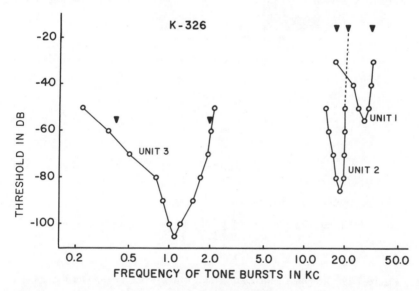

Figure 9.9 The tuning curves for Units 326-1, 2, 3.

The response patterns of these units are shown in Figures 9.8, 9.9, and 9.10. The solid triangles indicate the frequency and level of the tone bursts in Figures 9.8, 9.9, and 9.10. The dashed line indicates the presumed extent of the tuning curve for Unit 2.

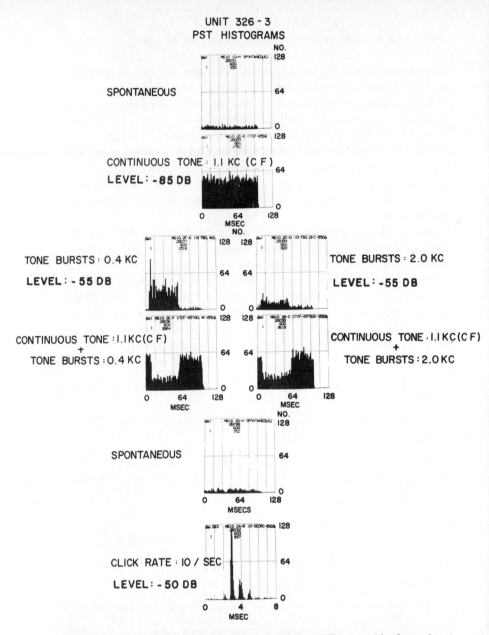

Figure 9.10 Response patterns of a unit with low CF to combined tone-burst and continuous-tone stimulation.

Rate of spontaneous discharges: 5.8 spikes/sec. The continuous tone at the CF and both tone bursts elicit positive responses when presented alone. The presentation of the tone burst in the presence of continuous tone results in partial reduction of the responses to continuous tone alone. The zero time of the histograms is 2.5 msec before the onset of the electric burst to the earphone. Stimuli: tone burst, 50-msec duration, 2.5-msec rise-fall time, 10 bursts/sec, −55 db; continuous-tone level: −85 db. The bottom histogram shows the response of the unit to clicks. Stimuli: clicks, 10/sec, −50 db.

play the main role (Fex, 1962). Finally, in a preliminary part of another study, we inserted a microelectrode into the peripheral stump of a severed eighth nerve and easily demonstrated the reduction of responses to a continuous tone at the CF by a tone burst not at the CF. (See Appendix B.)

The results described in this chapter indicate that the subject of complex stimuli requires a more thorough and more carefully controlled analysis than is possible within the framework of the present work. It may even be more efficient to continue the experimental studies within the framework of specific hypotheses concerning possible physiological mechanisms. Such an approach will at least serve to concentrate attention on fewer, and perhaps more tractable, experimental variables.

10. Discussion

10.1 Summary of Results

Many of the consequences of these experimental findings have
already been discussed briefly during the presentation of results, but
a number of general points deserve additional consideration. Before
proceeding to a discussion of the results, it may be helpful to sum-
marize those of the principal findings that will be discussed. The
numbers at the end of each point refer to the pages on which that
point is treated in more detail.

A. All units show some discharges in the absence of controlled
stimuli. The rate of this spontaneous activity may range from only a
few spikes/minute to over 100 spikes/sec. (P. 94.)

B. The responses of an individual primary unit to tones are restricted to certain ranges of stimulus frequencies. Within this range
there is a frequency of maximum sensitivity that we have called a
characteristic frequency (CF) because it is in some sense a funda-
mental characteristic of the unit. (Pp. 17, 84.)

C. The range of stimulus frequencies over which a unit will respond is narrow near the frequency of maximum sensitivity but
becomes broader as stimulus level is increased. At very high stimulus
levels the unit may respond to almost all audible frequencies below the
CF. (Pp. 79, 85, 88.)

D. For units with CF below 5 kc, the PST histograms of responses

118

to clicks show peaks separated by intervals that are equal to 1/CF. (Pp. 26, 27.)

E. For units with CF above 5 kc, there is usually one short-latency peak in the PST histograms of responses to clicks. There may however be small later peaks present at time intervals that do not correspond to 1/CF. (P. 29.)

F. The latencies of responses to clicks are short for all units with CF above 2 kc. For units with CF below 2 kc, the latencies are systematically related to CF; the units with lower CF show longer latencies. (Pp. 25, 26, 30.)

G. The shape of the PST histograms remains fairly constant over changes in both click level and click rate for any one unit. (Pp. 32, 49.)

H. For units with CF below 5 kc, the peaks in the PST histograms correspond to the rarefaction phase of the clicks. (Pp. 39, 42.) When units respond to tonal stimuli of frequencies below 5 kc, the discharges are time-locked to a particular phase of the tone. The exact phase is dependent upon stimulus level. (P. 79.)

I. When units respond to noise or tonal stimuli of frequencies above 5 kc, the discharges are irregular and have interval distributions resembling those of spontaneous activity. (Pp. 79, 95, 96, 107.)

J. A pragmatic "threshold" can be defined for each unit. These thresholds for different units may differ by as much as 40 to 60 db even for units with similar CF. (Pp. 84, 89, 91, 92.)

K. In response to tones the discharge rate of units increases with stimulus level until a maximum rate is reached. Further increases in stimulus level result in either no change in rate or a decrease in rate. Both the maximum rate and the level of tone for which the rate is maximum differ greatly for different units. (Pp. 79, 83.)

L. At the onset of a tone or noise there is a sharp rise in discharge rate followed by a gradual adaptation to a steady rate of discharge that is higher than the unit's rate of spontaneous discharge. (Pp. 68, 71, 73.)

M. The time pattern of the spontaneous discharges is irregular. The rate of spontaneous discharge bears no discernible relation to CF, a unit's sharpness of tuning, or state of the animal. For a given unit the rate of spontaneous discharges may be related to the threshold and the maximum discharge rate under continuous stimulation. (Pp. 17, 83, 94, 103.)

N. The baseline activity in PST histograms may be reduced at times corresponding to the condensation phase of stimuli. (Pp. 34, 35, 42.)

O. Responses to a continuous tone at the CF can be reduced in rate by presenting a tone burst of appropriate frequency and level. The tone burst can be so chosen that it increases a unit's discharge rate when presented in the absence of the continuous tone. (Pp. 112, 115.) These two-stimulus effects are demonstrable even after the auditory nerve is sectioned in the internal auditory meatus. (P. 117.)

10.2   The Relation of Response Patterns to the Neuroanatomy of the Cochlea

Individual fibers differ in their response characteristics, but many of the differences can be systematically related to CF [B,D,E,F,H,I].* If we know the CF of a unit, we can predict in a qualitative way certain characteristics of the time patterns of responses to simple stimuli, such as clicks [D,E,F,G], bursts of tones or of noise [L], and continuous tones or noise [H,I]. A unit's CF may be considered to be a reflection of its innervation longitudinally along the cochlear partition. Thus the locus of innervation is one important determinant of the time patterns of responses.

Because units with the same CF may have very different absolute thresholds [A], differences in threshold may relate to the innervation in the cochlea along a radial dimension [J]. This correlation of responses with the radial dimension of innervation has been attempted before in different ways. Tasaki (1954) suggested that fibers connected to inner hair cells may have higher thresholds than fibers connected to outer hair cells. Katsuki in 1961 believed that fibers with symmetric tuning curves innervate outer hair cells whereas fibers with asymmetrical tuning curves innervate inner hair cells. Later (1962), Katsuki, Suga, and Kanno came to the conclusion that for neurons with CF up to 6 kc, it was ". . . highly conceivable that the two subgroups of neurons with high and low thresholds correspond to those innervating inner and outer hair cells, respectively." Having reported "on" and "on-off" responses, suppression of spontaneous discharges, and inhibition of the response of primary neurons to tone bursts by a background sound, they suggested that these phenomena might be accounted for by the mode of innervation of spiral fibers on hair cells. Presumably, since the spiral fibers are said to terminate mainly on the outer hair cells, these authors would support the idea that the radial dimension would play an important role in the response characteristics of fibers.

In 1964, Nomoto, Suga, and Katsuki, strongly influenced by van Bergeijk's electronic models (1961) of the cochlea, attempted still

---

* Letters in brackets refer to the relevant principal findings at the beginning of this chapter.

another correlation. Differences in the slopes of functions relating discharge rate to stimulus level and frequency were postulated to be based on three anatomically distinct types of fibers: the external spiral, external radial, and internal radial fibers.

Our own data do not clearly support any of these previous suggestions. We are not convinced that a criterion has been found which allows us to divide primary units into two distinct types that can be correlated either with inner and outer hair cells or with radial and spiral fibers [J,K,L,M]. It might be prudent to defer speculation on this topic until some unsettled anatomical questions have been answered. What are the relative numbers of radial and spiral fibers? Is the distinction sharp or are there transitional types? Do the spiral fibers innervate hair cells all along their course after crossing the tunnel of Corti or do they travel long distances to innervate only a few outer hair cells? What are the distances that individual fibers travel within the cochlear partition? Can radial and spiral fibers originate from the same primary neuron? Are there some primary neurons that innervate only inner or only outer hair cells? Are there places where activity in one primary neuron can effect the activity in other primary neurons? What are the relations between efferent and afferent fibers within the cochlea? The answers to questions such as these should provide a firmer foundation for attempts to correlate the neuroanatomy and the electrophysiology of the auditory nerve.

In our present state of knowledge one should allow for the possibility that response characteristics of single fibers in the internal auditory meatus reflect the activity of intracochlear fibers that innervate several types of hair cells. Thus a single spiral ganglion cell might be connected to both inner and outer hair cells via some combination of spiral and radial fibers. It is possible that a very large number of fibers will have to be systematically studied before lawful relationships between anatomy and physiology are unequivocally verified.

10.3 Excitatory Mechanisms in the Cochlea

The study of how nerve impulses are generated within the cochlea is made particularly difficult by the extreme delicacy of the sensorineural apparatus. The very act of gaining direct access to the organ of Corti usually disrupts its normal functional state. However, it is possible that some insights into the cochlear excitatory mechanisms can be gained indirectly by studying the responses of the auditory nerve fibers. Fortunately our surgical exposure of the nerve does not injure the cochlear structures.

Consider what assumptions about the excitatory process might be required in order to generate models for the discharge patterns found in our study. On the basis of Flanagan's calculations for the impulse response of the basilar membrane (1962), Weiss (1964) developed a theoretical model for what is essentially a threshold device triggered by intracochlear mechanical movements. With the use of a large general-purpose computer, he attempted to simulate the PST histograms of click responses for units with low CF. By making certain assumptions about the transducer mechanism, he was able to obtain histograms that resembled those obtained from auditory nerve discharges but was unable to fit the detailed data describing changes in the histograms as a function of click level.

From such attempts it appears that one difficulty in generating specific models for events at the level of the auditory nerve is the wide choice of possible assumptions concerning the many physiological processes underlying excitation. It is difficult to characterize the contributions of any one stage in the chain of peripheral mechanisms. Matters would be considerably simplified if we could assume that the neural factors are similar to those of other receptor-nerve preparations, but even this step cannot be taken with full confidence (Gray, 1959; Hagiwara and Morita, 1963).

Whatever the nature of the excitatory mechanism, the intimate contact of peripheral nerve endings with hair cells clearly suggests the probable general location of the excitatory events. The hair cells in the cochlea are morphologically similar to those of the lateral-line organs of fish and amphibians and to the hair cells of the vestibular apparatus in most vertebrates. The hair cells of all these sensory systems are homologous in an evolutionary sense and have all been shown to be structurally asymmetric ("morphologically polarized") in the same way (Flock, Kimura, Lundquist, and Wersäll, 1962; Flock and Wersäll, 1962). Microphonic responses can be recorded from all the hair-cell systems, but the relation of these potentials to the excitatory mechanisms is still unclear.

Single-unit recordings from the lateral-line system have not been extensively studied. In the vestibular system fluid flow within the semicircular canals in one direction results in an increase in discharge rate of the nerve, while movement in the opposite direction diminishes the rate of activity (Lowenstein and Sand, 1940; Zotterman, 1943). Our data on auditory units show that movements of the cochlear partition that correspond to the rarefaction phase of the acoustic stimulus tend to increase discharge rate while movements that correspond to the condensation phase tend to reduce discharge rate [H]. Thus there would seem to be certain similarities in the excitatory mechanisms of hair-cell systems based on the directionality of the physical stimulus relative to the orientation of the hair cell. How the mechanism operates in detail is, however, still unknown.

Our findings on units with high CF introduce a further complication. Here the discharges do not appear to be phase-locked to the stimulus although the over-all rate of discharge is raised above the level of spontaneous activity. We may speculate that the decay time of the excitatory process is such that when the frequency of the acoustic stimulus rises above approximately 5 kc the effects of individual cycles merge: units no longer discharge synchronously with a particular phase of the stimulus but instead discharge whenever their recovery processes permit [E,I].

It is likely that as details of the anatomy and chemistry of the hair-cell–nerve-ending regions become better known, the role of chemical mediators will become increasingly important in our conceptions of both excitatory and recovery processes (Vinnikov and Titova, 1963). It is tempting to suggest that each stimulating phase results in a release of an excitatory chemical substance at the junction of the hair cell and nerve endings and that the effects of this substance last for some short period of time. Possibly the recovery process is associated with the destruction of this excitatory substance. As the rate of stimulation increases above 5 kc, the effects of each stimulating phase overlap that of the last and a pool of excitatory substance becomes continuously available. The response of the nerve cell would then be determined by the recovery properties of the unit, thus accounting for the similarity in the shapes of interval histograms of both spontaneous and continuously stimulated activity.

Electrophysiological attempts to study directly the excitatory mechanisms in the cochlea are usually based on measurements of cochlear potentials taken at locations remote from the presumed sources. Still unresolved is the question of whether the cochlear microphonics are directly involved in the excitation of nerve fibers (Davis, Fernandez, and McAuliffe, 1950; Davis, 1957). Similarly, the significance of summating or slow potentials remains conjectural (Davis, 1957; Davis, Deatherage, Rosenblut, Fernandez, Kimura, and Smith, 1958; Kiang and Peake, 1960). It is even conceivable that the excitatory processes do not have direct electrical correlates. At the present time we do not feel that we have sufficient evidence to assign to any one of the cochlear potentials a definite function in the excitatory mechanism.

10.4   Inhibitory Mechanisms in the Cochlea

The problem of what excites auditory nerve fibers raises the question of whether "inhibition" can also be demonstrated for these fibers. If by inhibition one simply means the reduction of spontaneous, baseline, or evoked activity by the introduction of appropriate stimuli, there are a number of inhibitory phenomena demonstrated in this study alone. The reduction of baseline activity by the condensation phase of clicks is one such phenomenon [N]; the effects of masking noise upon responses to the sound that is being masked may be another. A third kind of inhibitory phenomenon refers to the addition of a tone burst which can reduce or abolish the responses to a continuous tone at the CF for the duration of the tone burst [O]. All three inhibitory phenomena occur quite rapidly after the appropriate condition of stimulation has been established.

Fex (1962) has demonstrated that electrical stimulation of the olivo-cochlear efferent bundle will reduce or abolish sound-evoked activity in auditory primary units if the shocks are delivered at least 15 msec before the onset of the sound. He has also demonstrated that these efferent fibers respond to acoustic stimuli with latencies of 5 to 40 msec. Thus sound-induced inhibitory effects whose latency is much shorter than 20 msec may be considered to be different in mechanism from those studied by Fex.*

Table 10.1 summarizes the findings of various experimenters on the subject of inhibition in mammalian auditory nerve fibers. Papers by Galambos and Davis (1943, 1944), Katsuki, Sumi, Uchiyama, and Watanabe (1958), and Finck and Berlin (1965) have not been included because in these instances there is considerable doubt as to whether the units were actually auditory nerve fibers.

Short-latency inhibition of the responses to one tone by a second tone, such as we described in Chapter 9, have also been found by Nomoto, Suga, and Katsuki (1964) in the monkey and by Frishkopf (1964) in the little brown bat. From their descriptions there is little doubt that these phenomena resemble those in the cat. Since two-stimulus inhibition is present even after the auditory nerve is severed [O], this effect cannot be a result of efferent activity or middle-ear muscle activity. The failure of Kiang, Watanabe, Thomas, and Clark (1962) to find this type of inhibition in an earlier series of experiments may have been due to the fact that they kept the continuous

---

* It is also possible that the efferent system is inoperative if the animal is under barbiturate anesthesia. The anesthesia may also effectively eliminate the activity of middle-ear muscles in the cat (Simmons and Beatty, 1964).

TABLE 10.1 Types of Inhibitory Effects Reported on Mammalian Primary Units

Authors	Animal	Anesthesia	Electrodes	Effect of a Single Tone	Effect of Two Tones
Tasaki (1954)	Guinea Pig	Dial	3M KCl pipettes	No inhibition demonstrated	Not studied
Katsuki, Suga, and Kanno (1962)	Monkey	Nembutal	3M KCl pipettes	Suppression of activity between on and off responses to tone bursts	Not studied
Kiang, Watanabe, Thomas, and Clark (1962)	Cat	Dial	3M KCl pipettes	No inhibition demonstrated	No inhibition demonstrated
Rupert, Moushegian, and Galambos (1963)	Cat	Unanesthetized and Nembutal	Tungsten microelectrode	1. "Immediate inhibition" of spontaneous discharges (latency <20 msec). 2. Long-latency suppression of all discharges after initial increase in discharge rate.	Not studied
Nomoto, Suga, and Katsuki (1964)	Monkey	Nembutal	3M KCl pipettes	Not studied	Short-latency inhibition of responses to tone at CF by tone bursts on either side of CF. No effect of strychnine.
Frishkopf (1964)	Bat	Nembutal	3M KCl pipettes	Not studied	Short-latency inhibition of evoked activity by frequencies above and below excitatory range of unit.

tone and the tone bursts at comparable stimulus levels. Under these conditions two-stimulus inhibition is difficult to demonstrate because the effect is so small.*

In the present study we made extensive attempts to demonstrate inhibition of spontaneous activity by a single tone but did not succeed. Discharges elicited by a faint background noise can be inhibited by a tone burst, but this is undoubtedly a special case of the "two-stimulus" inhibition.†

The long-latency inhibition of spontaneous discharges reported by Rupert, Moushegian, and Galambos (1963) for unanesthetized cats is probably an effect of the efferent system, as they suggested. Unfortunately, they report no precise latency measurement for what they call "immediate inhibition." It may be that the unanesthetized animal generated its own noisy environment and immediate inhibition is a form of two-stimulus inhibition. Katsuki, Suga, and Kanno (1962) have reported inhibition of responses during presentation of single tone bursts. This single-stimulus inhibitory phenomenon seems to be associated with "on" and "on-off" responses to the tone bursts. We believe that their results may be explained by the fact that there is spread of energy to other frequencies at the turning on and off of a tone burst (Sandel and Kiang, 1961). Thus units that would not ordinarily respond to a tone burst of a particular frequency and level may well be excited by the turning on or off of the bursts. For a short tone burst any temporary depression of activity after the on responses may appear to be inhibition by the tone burst.

10.5   Conceptual Stages in the Production of Spike Discharges

The spontaneous activity of primary units is particularly interesting since the shape of the interval histogram may be considered similar for all units. We may think of spontaneous activity as being generated by a random process which is in some respects Poisson-like but which shows certain refractory properties (Rodieck, Kiang, and Gerstein, 1962). But what accounts for the large range in the rates of spontaneous activity that in our samples range from only a few per minute to over 100/sec?

We do not know where spontaneous discharges originate. We have presented evidence that tends to rule out ambient acoustic noise

---

* An interesting model to account for two-stimulus inhibition has been offered by Furman and Frishkopf (1964).

† The dangers associated with performing auditory experiments in a "noisy" room have rarely been so dramatically demonstrated.

as the causative factor for spontaneous activity. The reduction of baseline activity by the condensation phase of clicks and of tones suggests that spontaneous activity probably originates within the cochlea, somewhere within the cochlear partition. The absence of maintained reduction of baseline activity by tonal stimuli suggests a basic difference between the spontaneous and evoked discharges in the auditory nerve, with the spontaneous activity probably generated at a level central to where two-stimulus inhibition takes place.

If we postulate that spontaneous discharges result from "chemical noise" at the junction of hair cell and nerve ending, the two-stimulus inhibition must either take effect at the hair-cell level or be a reflection of some mechanical interaction. If, on the other hand, the spontaneous activity is generated at the level of fibers in the cochlea, the two-stimulus inhibition might represent events at the hair-cell–neural junction or any preceding stage. Whether the spontaneous activity is actually generated at the hair cells, nerve endings, peripheral axons, or some combinations of these levels, is not yet established (Pecher, 1939; Buller, Nicolls, and Strom, 1953; Verveen, 1960).

If the levels at which either spontaneous or evoked activity is generated were known, we could more nearly specify strategic targets for future investigations into the excitatory and inhibitory mechanisms in the cochlea. At the present we may define certain conceptual stages that represent key events in the chain leading ultimately to the production of spike discharges in auditory nerve fibers:

1. Mechanical vibration of the cochlear partition produces
2. mechanical movements at the hair-cell level, which activates
3. either mechanochemical or electrochemical processes at the hair cell, thus bringing about
4. the release of excitatory substances that stimulate
5. membrane changes in the nerve endings, which build up to generate
6. spike discharges that propagate along
7. the peripheral axonal extension,
8. the cell body of the spiral ganglion,
9. and the axons of the central extension where our microelectrodes are placed.

The usefulness of defining such stages is most obvious when we attempt to relate observed phenomena to possible physiological mechanisms. Our best guess based on the present, admittedly sparse, data is that spontaneous discharges are generated during Stage 4, 5 or 6;

two-stimulus inhibition occurs at Stage 2 or 3; reduction of baseline activity by the condensation phase of stimuli takes place at Stage 3 or 4; and the adaptation of responses probably occurs primarily during Stages 3, 4, 5, or 6 [L,O].

It is clear that the various conceptual stages will become more sharply defined as further data become available; for instance, Stage 4 will undoubtedly be broken up into many substages at a molecular level before long. The present guesses serve merely to indicate possible lines for future experimentation. Even though one might guess that two-stimulus inhibition occurs at Stages 2 or 3, mechanical factors and lateral inhibition between adjacent neurons have certainly not been conclusively eliminated. There is no need to assume that only one stage is critical for a given phenomenon; on the contrary, each phenomenon is the result of a chain of events for which certain links are critical in the sense that they have overriding significance for that particular phenomenon.

10.6   A Few Comments on the Role of Auditory Nerve Fibers in Mammalian Hearing

Although electrophysiological studies of single primary units are available for a teleost and the bullfrog, the role of airborne sounds in the life of these animals is not clearly understood (Enger, 1963; Frishkopf and Goldstein, 1963). It is doubtful if the peripheral apparatus in these animals can be directly compared to the mammalian cochlea. The similarity in structure of the cochlea in all mammals leads one to suspect that variations in auditory behavior in different species may be largely based on the differences in the development of the central nervous system to utilize the information transmitted by the auditory nerve. Consequently, one feels some reassurance in generalizing the results of studies on the peripheral auditory mechanisms of one mammalian species to another. It is of course necessary to take account of differences in the acoustic characteristics of the peripheral apparatus of different species (Greenwood, 1961). The cat appears to be more sensitive in the high-frequency region of the audiogram than man (Neff and Hind, 1955; Elliot, Stein and Harrison, 1960; Miller, Watson and Covell, 1963).

It is important to ask under what circumstances one might expect features of auditory behavior to correlate with activity in primary units. Clearly the envelope of the tuning curves of the most sensitive primary units [J] might be expected to resemble the behavioral audiogram, and it does for the cat (Miller, Watson, and Covell, 1963). However, there are also frequent attempts to account for the ability to make fine pitch discriminations with the sharpness of tuning of neural units despite the fact that tuning curves are sharpest near threshold [C] where pitch discrimination is poor (Rosenblith).

Another example where one might run into difficulties in relating psychophysical performance to peripheral auditory physiology is in the concept of critical bands. There have been numerous attempts to measure critical bands by psychophysical experiments and relate them to cochlear maps. (These attempts are summarized by Zwicker, Flottorp, and Stevens, 1957, and by Greenwood, 1961.) Apparently each critical band corresponds to equal distances along the cochlear partition.* If one should attempt to go further and relate critical bands to tuning curves of primary units, one encounters the difficulty that tuning curves become broader with increased stimulus level [C] whereas critical bands do not, within the stimulus range used in this study. Thus the critical bands may reflect processes that are located more in the central nervous system than processes at a strictly cochlear level.

Similarly, attempts to correlate loudness judgments with rates of discharge either in one fiber or in the whole auditory nerve meet with difficulties if one examines the details of both psychophysical and neurophysiological findings. It seems reasonable to adopt the position that psychophysical judgments do not necessarily bear simple relationships to events at the level of the auditory nerve. Certain tasks, such as signal detection, may be directly related to the presence or absence of responses in single auditory nerve fibers, but other tasks, such as pitch or loudness judgments, may depend on an elaboration of many different aspects of auditory nerve activity.

To illustrate, consider again the facts concerning pitch discrimination. According to a strict "place" theory the discrimination of different frequencies becomes a problem of sharpening the tuning of primary units. While cochlear mechanics provides a certain degree of tuning based on the spectral properties of the stimulus, inhibitory mechanisms may further sharpen the tuning of individual fibers. However a strict place theory appears to be untenable, and Wever (1949) has reviewed the evidence for a second principle in pitch determination based on time patterns of the responding units. It would appear that the psychophysical dimension of pitch, which has been frequently thought to be unitary, has at least two correlates at the auditory nerve

* Since critical bands vary by factors of 2 or 3, depending on how they are measured, the corresponding distance can be given as an order of magnitude only about 1 mm.

level (Licklider, 1951). It is the imposition of a single word "pitch" on the characterization of frequency discrimination that obscures the fact that several basically different mechanisms operate within the organism.

10.7 Some Remarks on the Pathology of Human Hearing in Relation to the Behavior of Single Auditory Nerve Fibers

We have examined briefly some possible relations between our findings and psychophysical performance in normal human subjects. It is obviously not possible to relate our findings at this time to all that is known about the pathology of human hearing. Such a task awaits authoritative treatment by competent clinicians. All we can do here is to touch upon a few points in the hope that others will go much further. On the basis of our own limited experience, we feel the need for caution in the interpretation of even the best-established clinical findings, since the locus and types of abnormalities are seldom simple to define.

Loss of sensitivity over virtually the entire audible range of frequencies is commonly attributed to middle-ear or inner-ear malfunction. Under these conditions the auditory nerve fibers fail to be stimulated either because sound conduction has been interrupted or other presumed abnormalities exist in the inner ear itself (Schuknecht and Igarashi, 1964).

Losses confined mainly to the high frequencies are commonly seen, for example, in some types of presbycusis and noise-induced hearing losses. Such losses seem different in kind from conductive losses. While our data do not directly illuminate this point, it may be worth noting that throughout this monograph we have been frequently led to making distinctions between the behavior of units with low CF and that of units with high CF.

Not only may sensitivity be abnormal, but in some pathological conditions, such as Ménière's disease, loss of sensitivity is frequently accompanied by loudness recruitment (Dix, Hallpike, and Hood, 1948). Under these circumstances there is an abnormally rapid growth of loudness with increased stimulus level so that at high stimulus levels the loudness judged by the defective ear may equal or exceed the loudness judged by a normal ear. In Ménière's disease there is distension of the scala media, with possible changes in the hair cells although the neural elements appear normal (Hallpike, and Cairns, 1938; Schuknecht, 1963). If there are systematic differences in the sensitivity of hair cells and if these differences are preserved in the auditory nerve, it is conceivable that damage selectively restricted to the most sensitive hair cells would functionally eliminate the most sensitive nerve fibers. The presence of recruitment suggests that, in making judgments of very loud sounds, the contribution of the most sensitive fibers should be less important than that of less sensitive fibers. According to this view, the neurophysiological basis of loudness estimation cannot be based only upon rates of discharge either in single fibers or groups of fibers but must also depend upon *which* fibers are being stimulated. Audiometric studies of cases in which there is evidence of direct damage to the auditory nerve without accompanying inner-ear pathology are rare. In cases of partial auditory nerve degeneration due to tumor pressure, there may be no loudness recruitment even when there is loss of sensitivity (Dix, Hallpike, and Hood, 1948). In some such cases the hair cells in the organ of Corti seem to be well preserved on histological examination. It is even possible to have normal threshold sensitivity with extensive nerve degeneration from tumor pressure or multiple sclerosis (Citron, Dix, Hallpike, and Hood, 1963). Apparently relatively few functioning nerve fibers are sufficiently well scattered throughout the cochlea. At the same time performances in speech discrimination tests may be poor (Walsh and Goodman, 1955; Jerger, 1960) so that there is definitely loss of some auditory capacity.

One particularly striking demonstration is found in cases of tumor pressure where a steady tone is frequently not heard at all after only a minute of exposure (Carhart, 1957; Jerger, 1960). Since normal auditory nerve fibers in the cat do not adapt to their spontaneous levels of discharges even after fifteen or more minutes, it may be worth exploring either more peripheral or more central factors in cases showing abnormal adaptation (Schubert, 1944; Dix and Hallpike, 1950; Dishoeck, 1953; Pestalozza and Cioce, 1962).

It should be evident from the preceding comments that the study of primary units alone will not provide a general theory of hearing. Human beings have the ability to perform a wide range of auditory functions with accuracy and subtlety. This ability is a property of the entire organism and not just the peripheral auditory mechanism. It is the task of later stages of the nervous system to reorganize the information delivered by auditory nerve fibers into more meaningful patterns and to channel the activity to appropriate effector organs. Knowledge of how this task is accomplished requires more detailed examination of activity in the central system (Kiang, 1965; Kiang, Pfeiffer, Warr, and Backus, 1965; Pfeiffer and Kiang, 1965).

Appendix A

The following table includes the raw data for a number of units that are used as the basis for many of the figures, relating CF, rates of spontaneous activity, and thresholds as determined by visual and auditory criteria. The data are obtained from cats with comparable N_1 thresholds (± 5 db) using condenser earphones as the stimulus source. An asterisk indicates that a tuning curve is available for that unit.

Unit	CF in kc	Spontaneous Rate in spikes/sec	Threshold in db at CF for Tone Bursts	Threshold in db for Clicks
293-1	4.00	—	−94	−68
293-2	2.50*	—	−109	−76
293-3	2.50*	—	−95	−68
293-4	8.00*	—	−92	−60
293-5	6.00	—	−75	−53
293-6	2.55	—	−95	−72
293-7	2.52*	59.0	−107	−70
293-8	0.42*	—	−74	−36
293-11	1.80*	—	−85	−73
293-12	2.40	—	−70	−43
293-13	3.90	—	−86	−60
293-14	2.40	—	−75	—
293-18	3.80	40.9	−83	−55
293-19	1.00	12.6	−75	−47
293-20	1.15	5.2	−64	−46

Unit	CF in kc	Spontaneous Rate in spikes/sec	Threshold in db at CF for Tone Bursts	Threshold in db for Clicks
293-21	1.50*	8.5	−67	−45
293-22	1.20	10.5	−63	—
293-24	1.00	1.9	—	—
294-1	0.40*	58.5	−95	−76
294-2	6.80	84.3	−77	−68
294-5	17.00	3.8	−56	−15
294-6	17.20*	62.0	−70	−47
294-11	6.70*	74.0	−91	−64
294-12	6.10	44.6	−81	−64
294-13	4.20	10.3	−79	−63
294-14	7.40*	93.1	−89	−57
294-15	9.50*	8.4	−84	−25
294-16	9.20	63.4	−82	−31
294-17	28.00*	12.1	−45	−12
294-18	15.10*	69.5	−67	−15
294-19	13.60*	45.7	−67	−42
294-20	15.70	76.6	−61	−40
294-21	15.00	69.5	−61	−41
294-22	13.70*	73.4	−79	−58
294-23	9.00*	61.6	−84	−54
294-24	0.48*	79.3	−93	−67
294-25	0.65	2.8	−76	−58
296-1	1.59*	1.4	−90	—
296-2	1.60*	1.7	−94	—
296-4	0.57*	84.0	−97	—
296-5	4.08*	—	−87	—
296-7	6.86*	63.7	−96	—
296-10	0.40	—	—	−65
296-11	12.47*	45.4	−93	−58
296-12	8.56*	38.8	−99	−64
296-15	5.16*	32.5	−65	—
296-16	6.99*	—	−88	—
296-17	8.15*	61.5	−101	−68
296-19	0.54*	60.5	−87	−65
296-20	1.48*	69.1	−91	−70
296-21	—	57.1	—	−70
296-22	0.42*	61.9	−86	−62
296-23	1.17*	—	−95	−65
296-24	1.79*	—	−94	−67
296-25	2.76*	41.3	−101	−72
296-26	3.22*	—	−91	−66
296-27	3.07*	—	−97	−68
296-28	2.61*	—	−89	−67
296-29	10.36*	34.1	−94	−54
296-30	19.76*	41.8	−71	−13
296-31	11.60*	24.1	−85	−51

Unit	CF in kc	Spontaneous Rate in spikes/sec	Threshold in db at CF for Tone Bursts	Threshold in db for Clicks
296-32	14.66*	44.7	−64	−37
297-3	2.30*	—	−104	—
297-4	7.38*	—	−97	—
297-5	19.09*	—	−86	−13
297-6	14.74*	—	−86	−52
297-8	5.82*	—	−102	−68
297-10	5.94	45.1	—	−67
297-11	0.59*	—	−95	−65
297-12	1.01*	32.9	−110	−75
297-15	1.31*	26.7	−104	−73
297-16	—	41.3	—	−71
297-18	13.73	—	−86	−50
297-19	8.06*	33.4	−103	−58
297-20	9.22	37.6	−106	−59
297-21	9.40*	—	−91	—
297-22	8.12	39.6	−104	−69
297-23	7.14	6.3	−89	−61
297-25	1.39	0.1	−89	−40
297-26	7.48*	18.7	−94	−61
297-27	10.19*	23.0	−98	−23
297-28	11.36*	61.1	−92	−50
297-29	8.00*	—	−105	−62
297-30	7.75*	39.2	−105	−65
297-32	8.46	—	−102	−61
297-33	1.23*	76.9	−106	−83
297-34	0.95*	1.2	−103	−67
297-35	0.33*	19.6	−97	−67
297-36	0.47*	99.6	−87	−70
297-37	4.80	—	−100	−67
297-38	4.98*	0.9	−89	−58
297-39	0.36	27.8	−94	—
297-40	0.86	0.2	−97	−57
297-41	10.35	51.7	−109	−56
297-42	11.22*	—	−95	−54
297-43	1.83*	60.6	−116	−85
298-2	0.54*	3.6	−97	—
298-3	0.67	—	−89	—
298-4	0.60*	—	−97	—
298-5	0.38	96.3	—	—
298-7	1.90*	—	−107	—
298-8	5.30*	—	−94	—
298-9	1.86*	—	−106	—
298-10	4.00*	8.2	−101	—
298-13	1.36*	—	−111	−78
298-14	0.66	56.7	−100	−72
298-15	0.62*	0.2	−77	−21

Unit	CF in kc	Spontaneous Rate in spikes/sec	Threshold in db at CF for Tone Bursts	Threshold in db for Clicks
298-17	1.15	—	−100	−78
298-18	1.60*	—	−94	−55
298-19	3.55*	58.0	−100	−67
298-20	3.67*	70.0	−99	−58
298-21	2.36	—	−91	−61
298-22	5.00*	—	−104	−66
298-23	0.42*	39.7	−80	−64
298-24	1.26	0.2	−96	−42
298-27	1.12*	68.9	−110	−80
298-28	1.88*	0.6	−94	−30
298-29	0.45*	54.8	−95	−52
298-30	2.75*	—	−92	−63
298-34	8.70*	—	−98	−55
298-39	1.72*	76.0	−111	−86
298-41	4.60*	55.7	−102	−69
298-42	—	51.8	—	−64
299-1	4.20*	37.1	−100	—
299-2	10.08*	81.0	−110	−69
299-3	27.50*	—	−79	—
299-4	9.40	71.5	−110	−69
299-5	6.15*	—	−117	−84
299-6	6.40	—	−103	−66
299-7	3.60*	38.2	—	−67
299-8	0.13*	59.0	−73	—
299-9	2.50*	61.7	−108	−79
299-10	2.70*	37.5	−108	−72
299-13	5.70*	—	−97	−68
299-14	4.40*	58.7	−105	−72
299-15	7.50	—	−109	−75
299-16	5.35*	38.1	−119	−79
299-17	10.05*	—	−99	—
299-18	9.40*	68.2	−111	−63
299-19	11.60*	38.3	−100	−59
299-20	6.00*	54.5	−115	−83
299-21	9.40*	67.6	−116	−63
299-22	8.90*	76.6	−108	−74
299-23	11.90*	52.5	−104	−61
299-24	11.00	54.7	−107	−65
299-25	10.05*	72.0	−113	−63
299-26	9.00*	65.5	−114	−69
299-27	10.06*	4.3	−100	−57
299-28	24.00*	57.3	−95	−62
299-29	5.20*	81.4	−113	−75
299-30	5.00*	4.6	−106	−80
299-31	8.60*	56.0	−115	−73
299-32	8.60*	65.0	−114	−69

Unit	CF in kc	Spontaneous Rate in spikes/sec	Threshold in db at CF for Tone Bursts	Threshold in db for Clicks
300-1	2.26	—	−100	−79
300-2	2.32	—	−100	−71
300-4	5.26	—	−87	−64
300-5	7.44	—	−86	−56
300-6	7.63	—	−92	−59
300-8	1.86	—	−82	−61
300-9	2.00	—	—	−59
300-10	1.69	8.2	−80	−58
300-11	1.43	—	−79	−57
300-12	1.72	55.4	−83	−60
300-13	1.95	33.9	−91	—
300-14	2.61	44.2	−77	−54
300-15	4.64	—	−74	−41
300-16	7.80	—	−88	−54
300-17	0.11	77.0	−57	−33
300-19	2.09	—	−76	−57
300-20	0.56	41.0	−100	−75
300-21	0.47*	52.5	−100	−68
300-22	2.30	41.0	−74	−45
300-23	5.40	20.3	—	−46
300-24	6.59	35.8	−90	−59
300-25	0.42	1.8	−89	−60
300-27	5.96	35.5	−89	−56
301-2	0.52*	—	−96	−69
301-3	0.46*	—	−94	−66
301-4	11.16*	—	−64	−30
301-5	16.61*	—	−50	−38
301-9	1.32*	—	−90	−56
301-11	1.00	—	−48	−37
301-18	6.55	—	−81	−48
301-21	0.71*	0.72	−83	−55
301-25	1.08	—	—	−59
301-28	1.03*	—	−86	−61
301-29	1.50*	—	−79	−50
303-1	0.43*	—	−93	−57
303-2	1.10*	—	−81	−55
303-3	1.32*	—	−83	−57
303-4	3.69*	—	−82	−49
303-5	3.96	—	−45	−42
303-6	0.43*	—	−94	−61
303-7	3.53	—	−72	−60
303-9	0.66*	—	−79	−52
303-10	2.26*	—	−68	−54
303-11	5.81*	—	−86	−62
303-13	1.85*	—	−66	−44
303-14	1.99*	—	−66	−40

Unit	CF in kc	Spontaneous Rate in spikes/sec	Threshold in db at CF for Tone Bursts	Threshold in db for Clicks
303-15	7.37*	—	−83	−46
303-16	8.26*	1.6	−74	−32
303-17	2.50	—	−58	−59
303-18	18.74	—	−77	−32
303-19	7.93*	—	−80	−54
303-20	5.88*	—	−84	−55
303-21	10.35	—	−80	−28
303-22	3.55*	—	−45	−25
303-23	0.32*	—	−81	−47
303-25	31.48*	—	−50	−14
303-26	1.43	—	−79	−61
303-27	1.02	—	−89	−65
303-28	28.55	—	−60	−14
303-30	27.38	—	−60	−25
303-33	1.06*	—	−84	−63
304-1	1.73*	—	−68	−40
304-2	5.36	—	−109	−81
304-3	2.09*	0.3	−98	−68
304-4	1.67	—	−95	−72
304-5	0.64	—	−100	−74
304-6	1.65	—	−83	−62
304-7	8.55*	—	−115	−81
304-8	8.10	—	−114	−80
304-9	9.08	—	−115	−72
304-10	8.31	—	−112	−77
304-11	26.05	1.9	−65	−30
304-13	10.36	—	−109	−56
304-16	6.25	—	—	−72
304-17	2.32	—	−70	−45
304-19	6.64	—	−112	−84
304-20	5.44	—	−93	−70
304-21	7.02	—	−105	−78
304-22	10.91	—	−97	−57
304-23	7.62	—	−110	−79
304-24	13.46	—	−81	−57
304-25	0.67	—	−84	−57
304-26	0.61	—	−88	−58
304-27	0.39	—	−79	−52
304-28	0.43	1.2	−79	−55
304-30	0.65	—	−94	−72
304-31	1.30*	—	−108	−80
304-32	2.50	—	—	−67
304-33	1.95	0.03	−76	−50
304-35	20.43*	—	−78	−25
304-36	4.80	—	−68	−60
304-38	7.59	—	−86	−45

Unit	CF in kc	Spontaneous Rate in spikes/sec	Threshold in db at CF for Tone Bursts	Threshold in db for Clicks
304-39	29.90	—	−64	−37
304-40	7.00	—	−80	−50
304-42	8.43	—	−112	−71
304-44	10.20	—	−105	−56
304-46	14.60	—	−68	−20
304-47	4.04	—	−84	−65
304-50	7.65	—	−121	−80
304-54	1.02	—	−101	−77
304-57	3.07	—	−90	—
304-58	2.66	—	−88	−68
304-61	7.49	—	−106	−75
305-1	2.17	81.1	−121	−84
305-2	2.06	2.3	−107	−67
305-6	0.40	14.6	−90	−64
305-7	1.95	65.8	−113	−77
305-11	16.27	97.4	−85	−56
305-12	5.91	20.0	−98	−71
305-14	10.16*	0.2	−74	−35
305-15	11.16	64.6	−115	−51
305-16	11.77	74.6	−96	−59
305-17	5.36	0.3	−71	−50
305-18	7.22	65.9	−82	−65
305-19	4.49	85.5	−90	−61
305-20	4.19	3.4	−67	−52
305-21	0.75	88.9	−94	−64
305-22	0.77	79.8	−100	−66
305-23	6.79	—	−106	−69
305-24	1.00	—	−90	−65
305-25	3.09*	94.4	−77	−55
305-26	3.45	2.9	−65	−50
306-1	1.64	53.3	−79	−56
306-2	1.65	1.4	−67	−46
306-3	1.75	62.3	−85	—
306-4	1.45	117.9	−88	−81
306-5	1.40	0.2	−75	−46
306-6	7.00	0.2	—	—
306-7	5.80	41.2	−89	−68
306-8	1.02*	7.6	−92	−59
306-9A	0.94	6.8	−90	−69
306-9	12.77	24.3	−95	−62
306-10	17.78	42.0	−92	−60
306-12	14.67	4.8	−85	−42
306-14	7.64	21.5	−98	−73
306-16	21.29*	0.8	−84	−13
306-17	1.79	4.8	−68	−48
306-18	1.91	63.2	−70	−50

Unit	CF in kc	Spontaneous Rate in spikes/sec	Threshold in db at CF for Tone Bursts	Threshold in db for Clicks
306-20	7.26	0.1	−80	−48
307-1	0.38	29.6	−67	−48
307-2	1.02	92.9	−84	−72
307-3	0.82	65.6	−80	−71
307-4	5.40	13.3	−80	−60
307-5	5.00	21.7	—	−50
307-7	1.49	—	−75	−57
307-9	—	75.2	—	−71
307-10	0.97	104.1	−88	−72
307-11	—	72.9	—	−68
307-12	2.20	12.0	−88	−67
307-13	2.00	—	—	−66
308-1	1.73	49.5	−74	−67
308-2	11.45	0.4	−80	−50
308-3	1.56	95.1	−99	−72
308-4	11.16	26.7	−93	−53
308-5	2.92	6.2	−70	−51
308-6	4.03*	5.9	−78	−57
308-7	0.34	—	−79	−68
308-8	—	4.2	—	−65
308-11	7.91	28.1	−97	−66
308-12	6.80	23.1	−92	−68
308-14	4.90	—	−77	−51
308.15	5.76	28.4	−94	−77
308-16	8.43	0.8	−84	−55
308-17	1.65	60.3	−97	−71
308-18	1.96	52.2	−98	−73
308-19	5.37	22.7	−83	−62
308-20	4.57	3.9	−70	−47
308-22	14.37	—	−67	−37
308-23	6.04*	17.3	−86	−60
308-24	0.35*	77.7	−79	−57
308-25	0.90	2.4	−88	−64
308-26	1.25	—	−91	−64
308-27	21.75	29.9	−68	−26
308-28	5.19	15.4	−86	−64
308-30	5.81	—	−85	−63
308-32	5.36	82.0	−81	−67
308-33	5.71	60.9	−91	−63
308-34	—	87.9	—	−61
308-35	—	44.8	—	−65
308-36	5.69	—	−78	−52
308-37	0.25*	1.7	−83	−53
308-38	0.29	69.2	−70	−44
308-39	1.04	63.7	−99	−80
308-40	1.07	0.2	−77	−50

Unit	CF in kc	Spontaneous Rate in spikes/sec	Threshold in db at CF for Tone Bursts	Threshold in db for Clicks
308-41	1.08	9.2	−95	−69
308-43	1.25	3.9	−93	−71
308-45	8.59	1.9	−88	−60
308-46	4.46	52.8	−73	−61
308-48	11.32	28.1	−86	−52
308-52	1.74	53.8	−86	−75
308-53	9.80*	33.5	−104	−59
308-54	9.56	46.9	−95	−60
308-55	7.27	—	−87	−64
308-56	11.06	30.6	−80	−30
308-57	7.66*	29.0	−91	−66
309-6	2.53	—	−94	—
309-8	1.45	6.2	−93	−68
309-11	1.21	—	−95	−74
309-13	0.83	—	−94	−69
309-14	0.57	—	−87	−60
309-15	2.42	—	−78	−55
309-17	0.70	—	−87	−68
309-18	1.42	39.4	−95	−69
309-19	6.61	—	−93	−70
309-21	0.63	—	−85	−63
309-22	1.45	5.2	−90	−67
309-23	1.43	16.0	−94	−68
309-24	1.61	2.6	−87	−66
309-25	1.92	11.6	−95	−71
309-26	2.05	64.3	−93	−74
309-27	1.88	65.7	−94	−76
309-28	2.06	3.0	−93	−67
309-29	2.24	9.5	−82	−60
309-30	2.74	17.5	−80	−61
309-31	0.39	58.4	−88	−69
309-32	6.49	—	−100	−71
317-2	0.82	51.2	−87	—
317-3	1.66	28.2	−85	—
326-1	28.00*	85.4	−55	—
326-2	18.50*	100.1	−85	—
326-3	1.10*	5.8	−105	—

Appendix B

Figure B.1   These data were obtained in a later series of experiments by Kiang and Sachs (1965).

The eighth nerve was sectioned in the internal auditory meatus and the micropipette inserted into the peripheral stump of the auditory nerve. There was no difficulty in recording from single units. As the figure shows, the interval histogram of spontaneous activity appears to be similar to those in Chapter 8: the response to a tone burst at the CF shows the characteristic transient peak in the PST histogram with adaptation to a steady level, and two-stimulus inhibition is present. The completeness of the surgical section was checked by histological examination. This experiment would seem to rule out the effect of efferent fibers in these phenomena.

(In the displays for this figure there are 200 bins in a histogram; each large division therefore contains 50 bins. The final bin is an "overflow" bin.)

UNIT 361-37
SEVERED EIGHTH NERVE

INTERVAL HISTOGRAM

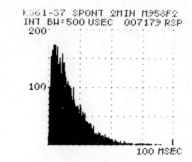

SPONTANEOUS

PST HISTOGRAM

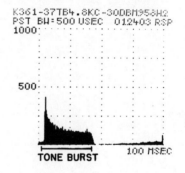

TONE BURST
4.8 KC (CF) -30 DB

PST HISTOGRAM

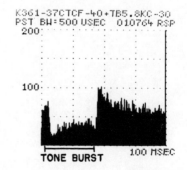

CONTINUOUS TONE
4.8 KC (CF) -40 DB
+
TONE BURST
5.8 KC -30 DB

References

Békésy, G. v. *Experiments in Hearing* (McGraw-Hill Book Co., Inc., New York, 1960), 745 pp.

van Bergeijk, W. A. "Analog of the external spiral innervation of the cochlea." *Kybernetik 1:* 102–107 (1961).

Buller, A. J., Nicholls, J. G., and Strom, G. "Spontaneous fluctuations of excitability in the muscle spindle of the frog." *J. Physiol. 122:* 409–418 (1953).

Carhart, R. "Clinical determination of abnormal auditory adaptation." *Arch. Otolaryngol. 65:* 32–39 (1957).

Citron, L., Dix, M. R., Hallpike, C. S., and Hood, J. D. "A recent clinico-pathological study of cochlear nerve degeneration resulting from tumor pressure disseminated sclerosis with particular reference to the finding of normal threshold sensitivity for pure tones." *Acta oto-laryngol. 56:* 330–337 (1963).

Contu, P. "Observations and considerations about the cochlear innervation of the cat." *Laryngoscope 58:* 586–595 (1958).

Davis, H. "Biophysics and physiology of the inner ear." *Physiol. Rev. 37:* 1–49 (1957).

Davis, H., Deatherage, B. H., Rosenblut, B., Fernandez, C., Kimura, R., and Smith, C. A. "Modification of cochlear potentials produced by streptomycin poisoning and by extensive venous obstruction." *Laryngoscope 68:* 596–627 (1958).

Davis, H., and Derbyshire, A. J. "The mechanism of auditory masking." *Amer. J. Physiol. 113:* 34 (1935).

Davis, H., Fernandez, C., and McAuliffe, D. R. "The excitatory process in the cochlea." *Proc. nat. Acad. Sci. 30:* 580–587 (1950).

Dishoeck, H. A. E. "Masking, fatigue, adaptation and recruitment as stimulation phenomena of the inner ear." *Acta oto-laryngol. 43:* 167–175 (1953).

145

Dix, M. R. and Hallpike, C. S. "Observations of the pathological mechanisms of conductive deafness in certain cases of neuroma of the VIII nerve." *Proc. roy. Soc. Med. 43:* 291–298 (1950).

Dix, M. R., Hallpike, C. S., and Hood, J. D. "Observations upon loudness recruitment phenomenon with especial reference to differential diagnosis of disorders of internal ear and eighth nerve." *Proc. roy. Soc. Med. 41:* 516–526 (1948).

Dowben, R. M., and Rose, J. E. "A metal-filled microelectrode." *Science 118:* 22–24 (1953).

Egan, J. P. "Independence of the masking audiogram from the perstimulatory stimulus." *J. acoust. Soc. Amer. 27:* 737–740 (1955).

Elliot, D. N., Stein, L., and Harrison, J. J. "Determination of absolute-intensity threshold and frequency-difference thresholds in cats." *J. acoust. Soc. Amer. 32:* 380–384 (1960).

Enger, Per Stockfleth. "Single unit activity in the peripheral auditory system of a teleost fish." *Acta physiol. scand. 59, Suppl. 210:* 1–48 (1963).

Engström, H., Ades, H. W., and Hawkins, J. E. "Cellular Pattern, Nerve Structures and Fluid Spaces of the Organ of Corti." In Neff, W. D. (ed.), *Contributions to Sensory Physiology 1* (Academic Press, Inc., New York, 1965), pp. 1–37.

Engström, H., and Wersäll, J. "Structure and innervation of the inner ear sensory epithelia." Vol. VI: *Int. Rev. Cytol.* (Academic Press, Inc., New York, 1958), pp. 535–585.

Fernandez, C. "The innervation of the cochlea (guinea pig)." *Laryngoscope 61:* 1152–1172 (1951).

Fex, J. "Auditory activity in centrifugal and centripetal cochlear fibres in cat, a study of a feedback system." *Acta physiol. scand. 55, Suppl. 189:* 1–68 (1962).

Finck, A., and Berlin, C. I. "Comparison between single unit responses in the auditory nerve and GSR determined thresholds in mice." *J. Auditory Research 5:* 1–9 (1965).

Flanagan, J. L. "Computational models for basilar-membrane displacement." *J. acoust. Soc. Amer. 34:* 1370–1376 (1962).

Fletcher, H. *Speech and Hearing in Communication,* 2nd ed. (Van Nostrand, New York, 1953), 480 pp.

Flock, Å., Kimura, R., Lundquist, P-G., and Wersäll, J. "Morphological basis of directional sensitivity of the outer hair cells in the organ of Corti." *J. acoust. Soc. Amer. 34:* 1351–1355 (1962).

Flock, Å., and Wersäll, J. "A study of the orientation of the sensory hairs of the receptor cells in the lateral line organ of fish, with special reference to the function of the receptors." *J. cell. Biol. 15:* 19–27 (1962).

Frank, K. "Identification and analysis of single unit activity in the central nervous system." In Field, J. (ed.), *Handbook of Physiology,* Section I. *Neurophysiology,* Vol. *I* (American Physiological Society, Washington, D. C. 1959), pp. 261–278.

Frishkopf, L. S. "Excitation and inhibition of primary auditory neurons in the little brown bat." *J. acoust. Soc. Amer. 36:* 1016 (1964).

Frishkopf, L. S., and Goldstein, M. H., Jr. "Responses to acoustic stimuli from single units in the eighth nerve of the bullfrog." *J. Acoust. Soc. Amer. 35:* 1219–1228 (1963).

Furman, G. G., and Frishkopf, L. S. "Model of neural inhibition in the mammalian cochlea." *J. acoust. Soc. Amer. 36:* 2194–2201 (1964).

Gacek, R. R., and Rasmussen, G. L. "Fiber analysis of the statoacoustic nerve of guinea pig, cat and monkey." *Anat. Rec. 139:* 455–463 (1961).

Galambos, R., and Davis, H. "The response of single auditory-nerve fibers to acoustic stimulation." *J. Neurophysiol. 6:* 39–57 (1943).

Galambos, R., and Davis, H. "Inhibition of activity in single auditory nerve fibers by acoustic stimulation." *J. Neurophysiol. 7:* 287–304 (1944).

Galambos, R., and Davis, H. "Action potentials from single auditory-nerve fibers." *Science 108:* 513 (1948).

Galambos, R., Schwartzkopff, J., and Rupert, A. "Microelectrode study of superior olivary nuclei." *Amer. J. Physiol. 197:* 527–536 (1959).

Gerstein, G. L., and Kiang, N. Y-S. "An approach to the quantitative analysis of electrophysiological data from single neurons." *Biophys. J. 1:* 15–28 (1960).

Gesteland, R. C., Howland, B., Lettvin, J. Y., and Pitts, W. H. "Comments on microelectrodes." *Proceedings of the IRE 47:* 1856–1862 (1959).

Glorig, A., and Nixon, J. "Distribution of hearing loss in various populations." *Ann. Otol. Rhinol. Laryngol. 69:* 497–517 (1960).

Goldstein, M. H., Jr., and Kiang, N. Y-S. "Synchrony of neural activity in electric response evoked by transient acoustic stimuli." *J. acoust. Soc. Amer. 30:* 107–114 (1958).

Gray, J. A. B. "Initiation of impulses at receptors." In Field, J. (ed.), *Handbook of Physiology,* Section I. *Neurophysiology,* Vol. *I* (American Physiological Society, Washington, D. C. 1959), pp. 123–145.

Greenwood, D. D. "Critical bandwidth and the frequency coordinates of the basilar membrane." *J. acoust. Soc. Amer. 33:* 1334–1356 (1961).

Hagiwara, S., and Morita, H. "Coding mechanisms of electroreceptor fibers in some electric fish." *J. Neurophysiol. 26:* 551–567 (1963).

Hallpike, C. S., and Cairns, H. "Observations on path of Ménière's syndrome." *J. Laryngol. Otol. 53:* 625–654 (1938).

Harrison, J., and Warr, W. B. "Second order neurons in the acoustic nerve." *Science 138:* 893–895 (1962).

Held, H. "Die Cochlea der Säuger und der Vögel, ihre Entwicklung und ihr Bau." In Bethe, A. (ed.), *Handbook Norm. Pathol. Physiol.* (J. Springer, Berlin, Vol. II, 1926), pp. 467–534.

Helmholtz, H. *On the Sensations of Tone as a Physiological Basis for the Theory of Music,* 2nd English ed. (Dover Publications Inc., New York, 1954), 576 pp.

Hood, J. D. "Studies in auditory fatigue and adaptation." *Acta otolaryngol., Suppl. 92:* 26–57 (1950).

Iurato, S. "Submicroscopic structure of the membranous labyrinth. 2. The epithelium of Corti's organ." *Z. Zellforsch 53:* 259–298 (1961).

Iurato, S. "Efferent fibers to the sensory cells of Corti's organ." *Exp. Cell Res. 27:* 162–164 (1962).

Jerger, J. "Audiological manifestations of lesions in the auditory nervous system." *Laryngoscope, 70:* 417–425 (1960).

Katsuki, Y. "Neural mechanism of auditory sensation in cats." In Rosenblith, W. A. (ed.), *Sensory Communication* (John Wiley & Sons, Inc., New York, 1961), pp. 561–584.

Katsuki, Y., Suga, N., and Kanno, Y. "Neural mechanism of the peripheral and central auditory system in monkeys." *J. acoust. Soc. Amer. 34:* 1396–1410 (1962).

Katsuki, Y., Sumi, T., Uchiyama, H., and Watanabe, T. "Electric responses of auditory neurons in cat to sound stimulation." *J. Neurophysiol. 21:* 569–588 (1958).

Kiang, N. Y-S. "The use of computers in studies of auditory neurophysiology." *Trans. amer. Acad. Ophthalmol. Otolaryngol. 65:* 735–747 (1961).

Kiang, N. Y-S. "Stimulus coding in the auditory nerve and cochlear nucleus." *Acta Otolaryngol. 59:* 186–200 (1965).

Kiang, N. Y-S., and Peake, W. T. "Components of electrical responses recorded from the cochlea." *Ann. Otol. Rhinol. Laryngol. 69:* 448–458 (1960).

Kiang, N. Y-S., Pfeiffer, R. R., Warr, W. B., and Backus, A. S. N. "Stimulus coding in the cochlear nucleus. *Ann. Otol. Rhinol. Laryngol. 54:* 463–485 (1965).

Kiang, N. Y-S., and Sachs, M. B. "Effects of acoustic stimuli on spontaneous spike discharges in auditory nerve fibers." *The Physiologist 8:* 208 (1965).

Kiang, N. Y-S., and Sandel, T. T. "Off-responses from the auditory cortex of unanesthetized cats." *Arch. ital. Biol. 99:* 121–134 (1961).

Kiang, N. Y-S., Watanabe, T., Thomas, E. C., and Clark, L. F. "Stimulus coding in the cat's auditory nerve: a preliminary report." *Ann. Otol. Rhinol. Laryngol. 71:* 1009–1026 (1962).

Kimura, R., and Wersäll, J. "Termination of the olivo-cochlear bundle in relation to the outer hair cells of the organ of Corti in the guinea pig." *Acta oto-laryngol. 55:* 11–32 (1962).

Lewy, F. H., and Kobrak, H. G. "The neural projection of the cochlear spirals on the primary acoustic centers." *Arch. Neurol. Psychiat. 35:* 839–852 (1936).

Licklider, J. C. R. "Basic Correlates of the Auditory Stimulus." In Stevens, S. S. (ed.) *Handbook of Experimental Psychology* (John Wiley & Sons, Inc., New York, 1951), pp. 985–1039.

Lorente de Nó, R. "Anatomy of the eighth nerve. The central projection of the nerve endings of the internal ear." *Laryngoscope 43:* 1–38 (1933).

Lorente de Nó, R. "The sensory endings in the cochlea." *Laryngoscope 47:* 373–377 (1937).

Lowenstein, O., and Sand, A. "The individual and integrated activity of the semicircular canals of the elasmobranch labyrinth." *J. Physiol. 99:* 89–101 (1940).

Miller, J. D., Watson, C. S., and Covell, W. P. "Deafening effects of noise on the cat." *Acta oto-laryngol., Suppl. 176:* 1–91 (1963).

Møller, A. R. "An experimental study of the acoustic impedance of the middle ear and its transmission properties." *Acta oto-laryngol. 60:* 129–149 (1965).

Neff, W. D., and Hind, J. E. "Auditory thresholds of the cat." *J. acoust. Soc. Amer. 27:* 480–483 (1955).

Nomoto, M., Suga, N., and Katsuki, Y. "Discharge pattern and inhibition of primary auditory nerve fibers in the monkey." *J. Neurophysiol. 27:* 768–787 (1964).

Peake, W. T., and Kiang, N. Y-S. "Cochlear responses to condensation and rarefaction clicks." *Biophys. J. 2:* 23–34 (1962).

Peake, W. T., Goldstein, M. H., Jr., and Kiang, N. Y-S. "Responses of the auditory nerve to repetitive acoustic stimuli." *J. acoust. Soc. Amer. 34:* 562–570 (1962).

Peake, W. T., Kiang, N. Y-S., and Goldstein, M. H., Jr. "Rate functions for auditory nerve responses to bursts of noise: Effect of changes in stimulus parameters." *J. acoust. Soc. Amer. 34:* 571–575 (1962).

Pecher, C. "La fluctuation d'excitabilité de la fibre nerveuse." *Arch. int. Physiol. 49:* 129–152 (1939).

Pestalozza, G., and Cioce, C. "Measuring auditory adaptation: the value of different clinical tests." *Laryngoscope 72:* 240–261 (1962).

Pfeiffer, R. R., and Kiang, N. Y-S. "Spike discharge patterns of spontaneous and continuously stimulated activity in the cochlear nucleus of anesthetized cats." *Biophys. J. 5:* 301–316 (1965).

Polyak, S. L., McHugh, G., and Judd, D. K. *The Human Ear in Anatomical Transparencies* (Sonotone, Elmsford, N. Y., 1946), 136 pp.

Ramón y Cajal, S. *Histologie du Système Nerveux de l'Homme et des Vertébrés* (A. Maloine, Paris, 1909–11).

Rasmussen, G. L. "Efferent fibers of the cochlear nerve and cochlear nucleus." In Rasmussen, G. L. and Windle, W. F. (eds.), *Neural Mechanisms of the Auditory and Vestibular Systems* (Charles C. Thomas, Springfield, Ill., 1960), pp. 105–115.

Retzius, G. *Das Gehörorgan der Wirbeltiere, Vol. II, das Gehörorgan der Reptilien, der Vögel, und der Säugetiere* (Samson & Wallin, Stockholm, 1884).

Rodieck, R. W., Kiang, N. Y-S., and Gerstein, G. L. "Some quantitative methods for the study of spontaneous activity of single neurons." *Biophys. J. 2:* 351–368 (1962).

Rosenblith, W. A. "Auditory masking and fatigue." *J. acoust. Soc. Amer. 22:* 792--800 (1950).

Rosenblith, W. A. "Relations between auditory psychophysics and auditory electrophysiology." *Trans. N. Y. Acad. Sciences.* Ser. II, Vol. *19:* 650–657 (1957).

Rosenblith, W. A. (ed.) *Processing Neuroelectric Data* (M. I. T. Press, Cambridge, Mass., 1959).

Rosenblith, W. A., and Rosenzweig, M. R. "Latency of neural components in round window response to pure tone." *Fed. Proc. 11:* 132 (1952).

Rosenbluth, J. "The fine structure of acoustic ganglia in the rat." *J. cell. Biol. 12:* 329–359 (1962).

Rupert, A., Moushegian, G., and Galambos, R. "Unit responses to sound from auditory nerve of the cat." *J. Neurophysiol. 26:* 449–465 (1963).

Sandel, T. T., and Kiang, N. Y-S. "Off-responses from the auditory cortex of anesthetized cats: effects of stimulus parameters." *Arch. ital. Biol. 99:* 105–120 (1961).

Sando, Isamer. "The anatomical interrelationships of the cochlear nerve fibers." *Acta oto-laryngol. 59:* 417–436 (1965).

Schubert, K. Hörermüdung und Hördauer." *Z. Hals-Nas.-Ohrenheilk. 51:* 19–74 (1944).

Schuknecht, H. F. "Neuroanatomical correlates of auditory sensitivity and pitch discrimination in the cat." In Rasmussen, G. L. and Windle, W. (eds.), *Neural Mechanisms of the Auditory and Vestibular Systems* (Charles C. Thomas, Springfield, Ill., 1960).

Schuknecht, H. F. "Ménière's Disease: a correlation of symptomatology and pathology." *Laryngoscope 73:* 651–665 (1963).

Schuknecht, H. F. and Igarashi, M. "Pathology of slowly progressive sensori-neural deafness." *Trans. amer. Acad. Ophthalmol. Otolaryngol. 68:* 222–242 (1964).

Siebert, W. M. "Models for the dynamic behavior of the cochlear partition." *Quarterly Progress Report,* No. *64* (Research Laboratory of Electronics, M. I. T., 1962), pp. 242–258.

Simmons, F. B., and Beatty, D. L. "Habituation (adaptation) in the middle-ear muscle reflexes of the cat." *Acta oto-laryngol. 57:* 89–96 1964).

Sivian, L. J., and White, S. D. "On minimum audible sound fields." *J. acoust. Soc. Amer. 4:* 288–321 (1933).

Smith, C. A. "Innervation pattern of the cochlea, the internal hair cell." *Ann. Otol. Rhinol. Laryngol. 70:* 504–528 (1961).

Smith, C. A., and Rasmussen, G. L. "Recent observations on the olivo-cochlear bundle." *Ann. Otol. Rhinol. Laryngol. 72:* 489–506 (1963).

Smith, C. A., and Sjöstrand, F. S. "Structure of the nerve endings on the external hair cells of the guinea pig cochlea as studied by serial sections." *J. Ultrastructure Res. 5:* 523–556 (1961).

Spoendlin, H. H., and Gacek, R. R. "Electromicroscopic study of the efferent and afferent innervation of the organ of Corti in the cat." *Ann. Otol. Rhinol. Laryngol. 72:* 660–686 (1963).

Stevens, S. S., and Davis, H. *Hearing. Its Psychology and Physiology* (John Wiley & Sons, Inc., New York, 1938).

Stevens, S. S., and Newman, E. B. "On the nature of aural harmonics." *Proc. nat. Acad. Sci., Wash. 22:* 668–672 (1936).

Tasaki, I. "Properties of myelinated fibers in frog sciatic nerve and in spinal cord as examined with microelectrodes." *Jap. J. Physiol. 3:* 73–94 (1952).

Tasaki, I. "Nerve impulses in individual auditory nerve fibers of guinea pig." *J. Neurophysiol. 17:* 97–122 (1954).

Tasaki, I. "Afferent impulses in auditory nerve fibers and the mechanism of impulse initiation in the cochlea." In Rasmussen, G. L. and

Windle, W. (eds.), *Neural Mechanisms of the Auditory and Vestibular Systems* (Charles C. Thomas, Springfield, Ill., 1960).

Tasaki, I., and Davis, H. "Electric responses of individual nerve elements in cochlear nucleus to sound stimulation (guinea pig)." *J. Neurophysiol. 18:* 151–158 (1955).

Teas, D. C., Eldredge, D. H., and Davis, H. "Cochlear responses to acoustic transients: an interpretation of whole-nerve action potentials." *J. acoust. Soc. Amer. 34:* 1438–1459 (1962).

Verveen, A. A. "On the fluctuation of threshold of the nerve fibre." In Tower, D. B. and Schadé, J. P. (eds.), *Structure and Function of the Cerebral Cortex* (Elsevier Publishing Co., Amsterdam, 1960).

Vinnikov, J. A., and Titova, L. K. "Cytophysiology and cytochemistry of the organ of Corti: a cytochemical theory of hearing." In Bourne, G. H. and Danielli, J. F. (eds.), *Int. Rev. Cytol. 14:* 157–191 (1963).

deVries, H. L. "Brownian motion and the transmission of energy in the cochlea." *J. acoust. Soc. Amer. 24:* 527–533 (1952).

Walsh, T. E., and Goodman, A. "Speech discrimination in central auditory lesions." *Laryngoscope 65:* 1–8 (1955).

Weiss, T. F. "A model for firing patterns of auditory nerve fibers." *Technical Report No. 418,* Research Laboratory of Electronics, M. I. T., 1964.

Wever, E. G. *Theory of Hearing* (John Wiley & Sons, Inc., New York, 1949), 484 pp.

Wever, E. G., and Lawrence, M. *Physiological Acoustics* (Princeton University Press, Princeton, N. J., 1954), 454 pp.

Zotterman, Y. "The microphonic effect of teleost labyrinths and its biological significance." *J. Physiol. 102:* 313–318 (1943).

Zwicker, E., Flottorp, G., and Stevens, S. S. "Critical bandwidth in loudness summation." *J. acoust. Soc. Amer. 29:* 548–557 (1957).

Index

Some words such as characteristic frequency are used so extensively in this monograph that only the pages on which they are defined are listed.